ELECTRONIC
FOR
COMPUTER
OF MODEL

CW00401623

ELECTRONIC CIRCUITS
FOR THE
COMPUTER CONTROL
OF MODEL RAILWAYS

by

R. A. PENFOLD

BERNARD BABANI (publishing) LTD
THE GRAMPIANS
SHEPHERDS BUSH ROAD
LONDON W6 7NF
ENGLAND

PLEASE NOTE

Although every care has been taken with the production of this book to ensure that any projects, designs, modifications and/or programs etc. contained herewith, operate in a correct and safe manner and also that any components specified are normally available in Great Britain, the Publishers do not accept responsibility in any way for the failure, including fault in design, of any project, design, modification or program to work correctly or to cause damage to any other equipment that it may be connected to or used in conjunction with, or in respect of any other damage or injury that may be so caused, nor do the Publishers accept responsibility in any way for the failure to obtain specified components.

Notice is also given that if equipment that is still under warranty is modified in any way or used or connected with home-built equipment then that warranty may be void.

First Published — March 1987
Reprinted — February 1989

British Library Cataloguing in Publication Data
Penfold, R. A.
    Electronic circuits for the computer
    control of model railways.
    1. Railroads ——— Models
           ——— Data processing
    2. Microcomputers
    I. Title
    625 1'9'0285416   TF197

    ISBN 0 85934 154 2

Printed and Bound in Great Britain by Cox & Wyman Ltd, Reading

Preface

Home computers are a relatively recent invention, but computer control techniques have been in existence for many years, and model railway enthusiasts were possibly the first hobbyists to make use of them. I remember attending a model railway exhibition over twenty years ago where a layout which ran automatically to a preprogrammed time-table was demonstrated. This was not only before the home computer era, but was before the invention of the microprocessor, or even the integrated circuit come to that. Automatic control of layouts had to be achieved using custom built logic circuits with a large number of discrete transistors and diodes, or a combination of electronics and electro-mechanical devices.

These days a home computer can be used as the basis of a computer controlled layout, and sophisticated control is relatively easy to achieve. Quite simple programs are normally all that is required, but the main difficulty is in interfacing the computer to the layout. There is relatively little ready-made equipment available which is suitable for this task, but fortunately, it is not difficult to build suitable interfaces, and they can be surprisingly inexpensive. The interfaces described in this book include various types of controller (including a high quality pulsed type), plus circuits for train position sensing, signal control and electric points control.

Although there is perhaps a tendency to think in terms of massive layouts when the subject of computer controlled model railways is raised, it is not something which lends itself only to complex and expensive layouts. Even something quite basic like and oval of track with a single siding can be given a new dimension by adding computer control, and there is plenty of fun to be had from relatively simple set-ups.

R. A. Penfold

CONTENTS

Chapter 1

POWER CONTROLLERS

It is possible to fully computerise a model railway so that, once it has been programmed, the points, signals, sound effects and the trains themselves all operate automatically. However, rather than jump straight in at the deep end in attempting to run everything under the control of a computer, it is perhaps better to take a more gradual approach, and the obvious starting point is with the control of the train or trains. There are a number of different ways of tackling this problem, and the best one to choose depends on whether simple or sophisticated control of the train is required. Also, whether you are a software expert who would prefer to use relatively simple hardware with complex software to make it perform well or would prefer somewhat more complex hardware which needs only very simple driving software.

We will consider several different approaches here, and there should be something to suit the requirements of practically anyone, including those who require sophisticated controllers which provide realistic results. However, before describing some controller circuits it is first necessary to at least take a brief look at the way in which signals to operate a controller can be taken from a home computer, and also how the computer can read signals from sensors.

Computer Basics

There is insufficient space available here to give a detailed description of computer interfacing techniques, but some of the more important basics of the subject will be covered. Those who are already familiar with computer interfacing should skip over this section, while those who are not should try to grasp the points covered here before trying to interface any circuits to their computer. There are books which provide further information on computer interfacing, including BP130, *Micro Interfacing Circuits – Book 1* and BP131, *Micro Interfacing Circuits – Book 2* from the same publisher and author as this publication.

Virtually every computer has some form of expansion port, but it is not usually possible to directly take signals from these which can be used to control electric motors and other devices. Some form of add-on board is required, and for our purposes a PIA

1

(parallel interface adaptor) board is the most suitable. Some computers do have a suitable built-in port in the form of a user port, and the Commodore 64 and BBC machines are two examples of computers which fall into this category. It is often possible to use a Centronics type parallel printer port as an output to drive simple add-ons, and a port of this type can usually provide one or two inputs as well, but a reasonable knowledge of your computer's hardware would be needed in order to use its printer port as a general purpose digital port. It would obviously be unwise to experiment with expensive computer equipment unless you have a reasonable understanding of what you are doing.

With most general purpose parallel interfaces it is not normally a matter of having some input lines and some separate output lines. A more common arrangement is to have a number of lines which can be set as inputs or as outputs, as required. In some cases each individual line can be set as an input or an output, but in others there might be (say) 16 lines divided into two groups of 8, with each group having to be set as all inputs or all outputs. If your computer has a built-in user port of some kind then the manual should give at least basic details on how to set it up and use it, or there should be an advanced manual or other publication which gives details of this. If you obtain an add-on parallel interface for your computer then this should certainly be supplied with some form of documentation giving concise information on how to set up and use the unit.

As a typical example of a parallel port which illustrates some fundamental points very well, we will consider the user port of the BBC model B computer (the B+, B+128, and Master series computers are all fitted with exactly the same port). Figure 1 shows the lines available on this user port, and one row is devoted to only the ground (earth or negative supply rail) and +5 volt supply rail. The inclusion of a 5 volt supply output is a common feature of user and parallel ports, and a very useful one as it often eliminates the need for any add-ons connected to the port to have their own power supply. However, bear in mind that there is a limit to the amount of power that can be tapped off from the computer. With the BBC model B, assuming that the power port is not being used to power disc drives, a generous 1.25 amps is available, but most other computers can only provide about a tenth of this current level. Sometimes other supply voltages are available from the computer, and although the user port provides only the +5 volt output, the power port additionally furnishes

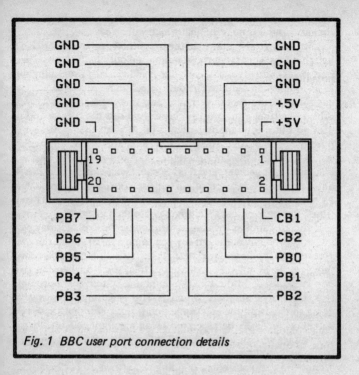

Fig. 1 BBC user port connection details

+12 and −5 volt outputs. Again, there is a limit to the current that can be taken from any additional supply outputs, and in this case the relevant figures are 1.25 amps and 50 milliamps. It is especially important to bear in mind the limitations of power supply outputs in an application such as model train control where high currents can be involved. In general the computer will be able to support any electronics that are connected to the user or other form of parallel port, but devices such as solenoids and electric motors may well require too much current and in most instances will require a separate power source.

Lines CB1 and CB2 are what are termed "handshake" lines, and they are designed for use in regulating the flow of data into or out of the user port. In a model train control application they will often be of little value, although CB2 can be used as a general purpose output if desired (CB1 can only function as an input).

Using these lines is something less than completely straightforward, and it is not a subject which will be covered here.

The lines of most interest in the present context are PB0 to PB7, and these are general purpose inputs and outputs. The BBC user port is very versatile, and each line is individually programmable as an input or an output. The data direction register is used to set each line to the required mode, and this register is at address &FE62. Setting a bit of this register to 0 sets the corresponding user port line as an input, setting a bit to 1 sets the relevant user port line as an output. At switch-on all the bits of this register are set to 0, and all the lines therefore start out as inputs. This is a common arrangement, and it is a sort of simple safety measure. If any outputs are connected to the user port it ensures that at switch-on they are driving inputs, and the potentially disastrous situation where outputs are driving outputs is avoided.

If you are familiar with binary arithmetic the explanation given above is probably sufficient for you to be able to set up the user port lines as inputs and (or) outputs, as desired. If binary is something you have not yet encountered, then some further explanation is required. In the binary numbering system there are only two single digit numbers; 0 and 1. This is a convenient way of doing things from the electronic point of view in that these two numbers can easily be represent by an electronic circuit, with a low voltage of typically around 0 to 0.8 volts corresponding to 0 (often called "logic 0" or just "low"), and a higher voltage of around 2.5 to 5 volts corresponding to 1 ("logic 1" or "high"). A detailed explanation of the binary numbering system would be out of place here, and really all that is needed is a basic understanding of how decimal numbers relate to binary numbers, which then makes it easy to understand the relationship between decimal numbers and the logic states on the user port lines that they produce.

Here things are simplified by the fact that we are only dealing with eight bit (Binary digIT) numbers as there are only eight user port lines. This gives a binary number range of 00000000 to 11111111, which is equivalent to a range of 0 to 255 in the ordinary decimal numbering system.

In effect, a binary digit set at 0 contributes 0 to the total value, while a bit which is set at 1 corresponds to a particular decimal number, and contributes that number to the total value. Working from the extreme right hand column towards the left, the numbers are 1, 2, 4, 8, 16, etc. The following list gives the number to which each user port line corresponds:-

PB0	1	PB4	16
PB1	2	PB5	32
PB2	4	PB6	64
PB3	8	PB7	128

Relating this to the data direction register and the value to be written to it to provide the required set of input/output lines, is just a matter of deciding which lines are to be outputs, looking up the corresponding numbers for these lines in the above list, and then writing the total of these numbers to the data direction register. As a simple example, assume that PB0 to PB3 are to be set as outputs and that the other four lines are to be inputs. Looking up the numbers for PB0 to PB3 in the list gives 1, 2, 4, and 8, which gives a total of 15. This is the value that would be written to the data direction register, and with BBC BASIC this would be done with the command:-

?&FE62=15

The BBC machine is unusual in that a question mark ("?") is used ahead of a number to indicate that it is an address. With most other 6502 based computers (or types with a 6502 bus compatible microprocessor) the POKE instruction is used to write values to output devices. With Z80 based computers it is usually the OUT command that must be used. In the majority of cases the user port lines are either all set as inputs, or are all set up as outputs, which requires data direction register values of 0 and 255 respectively.

It is important to realise that the data direction register is only used for setting up the user port with the desired combination of input and output lines, and that data is not read from or written to the port at this address. The peripheral register, which can be regarded as the user port lines, is at address &FE60. This register can be read with the instruction:-

PRINT ?&FE60

If a line is low it contributes zero to the returned value. If a line is high, the number contributed to the returned value depends on the line concerned, and can be found by refering to the list

5

provided earlier (e.g. PB7 adds 128 to the returned value when it is set high). With all the lines left in their default (input) state, trying the instruction given above will provide an answer of 255, since the inputs have pull-up resistors which take them high if they are simply left floating. Taking in data from sensors which indicate the position of the train is often essential, but for the moment we are more concerned about writing data to the user port than reading from it.

Writing 0 to a bit of the peripheral register sets the corresponding user port line low – writing a 1 to a bit of the peripheral register sets the appropriate line high. This does, of course, assume that the line concerned has first been set as an output, and data written to lines set as inputs has no effect. Looking at things in the most simple possible terms, the correct value to write to the peripheral register can be calculated by first deciding which lines are to be set high, looking up the values for these in the list given previously, and then adding up the numbers to give the total value to be written to the peripheral register. In other words it is the same as calculating the value to be written to the data direction register, but it is lines being set high instead of lines being designated as outpus in this case.

As a simple example, to set PB4 to PB7 all high with the other lines being set low, a value of 240 would be needed ($16+32+64+128=240$).

Relay Control

The ability to switch output lines between 0 volts or so and around 3 to 5 volts does not permit the direct control of small electric motors. On the face of it this should be possible, since a low voltage of about one volt or less is inadequate to cause most small electric motors to operate at all, whereas about 3 to 5 volts will properly drive some of the lower voltage types. One difficulty in a train controller application is simply that most model engines have a 12 volt motor. The main problem though, is simply that the user port output lines (and those of any comparable port) are only intended for driving digital inputs on add-on circuits, and have only a modest current drive capability. The precise drive current depends on the particular device used to provide the output lines, but would typically only be a few milliamps with one of the lines short circuited to one or other of the supply rails. Small electric motors require around one hundred times this current level, and with the output being loaded down by no more than about 20 to

30% so as to leave an adequate drive voltage.

A relay represents the most simple means of controlling an electric motor from a digital output, but in most cases the relay can not be directly driven from the output lines. Again, it is a matter of insufficient drive current being available, although in this case the current requirement is somewhat less, with a typical low voltage relay requiring a drive current of only about 40 milliamps for reliable operation. There are in fact some relays that can be directly driven from the types of digital output that have relatively high drive currents, but the relay contacts mostly have inadequate ratings to be of any real use in this application.

Relay contact ratings are something that has to be carefully watched when driving an inductive load such as a solenoid or an electric motor, as under these circumstances the maximum permissible current and voltage ratings are generally substantially less than for resistive loads. When a solenoid is activated or deactivated there is a tendency for the rapidly changing magetic field to generate a fairly high voltage across the coil, and this voltage can lead to contact sparking at the switch or relay contacts. This tends to cause corrosion and a high contact resistance when the contacts are closed, and in an extreme case it is even possible for the contacts to become welded together. I would therefore strongly recommend the use of a relay with generous contact ratings when driving any highly inductive load.

The circuit shown in Figure 2 enables a relay to be controlled from a digital output, and in order to control several motors it is merely necessary to use several of these circuits driven from separate digital output lines. Transistor Tr1 operates as a straightforward common emitter amplifier/switch which is switched on when the input line goes high. R1 and R2 act as a potential divider which ensures that the base voltage fed to Tr1 when the input is in the low state is not sufficient to bias the device into conduction and hold the relay switched on. D1 is the protection diode which is almost invariably included when a semiconductor switching device is used to control a highly inductive load.

It was pointed out earlier that a high voltage can be generated across a solenoid when it is switched off, due to the magnetic force around the coil rapidly decaying and inducing the voltage in the coil. With a mechanical switch this gives the problem of sparking at the contacts, but with semiconductor switching it is more a problem of instant destruction of the switching device, and possibly of other semiconductor components in the circuit as well.

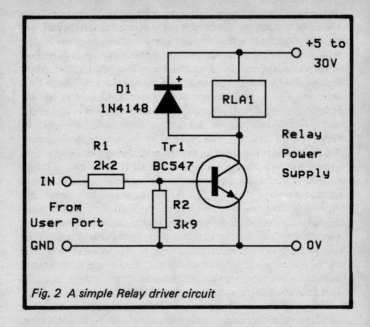

Fig. 2 A simple Relay driver circuit

The voltage spike is at a fairly high impedance and of opposite polarity to the supply. D1 has the effect of virtually short circuiting the pulse, clipping it at an innocuous 0.6 volts or so. The high source impedance of the pulse ensures that D1 does not receive a fatally high pulse of current. Do not be tempted to omit protection diodes such as D1, since this would almost certainly result in the switching device being short lived, and it could just possibly result in expensive damage to other components in the system. Semiconductor devices are very intolerant of even moderately high voltages for even very short periods of time.

The relay and driver circuit are shown as having a separate power supply in Figure 2, but if the computer or other controlling circuit can provide a suitable supply voltage at an adequate current then this can be used. In many cases the controlling equipment will only provide a 5 volt supply output, and this is rather restrictive in that there are few readily available relays that are guaranteed to operate properly with such a low supply voltage. Some relays which have a nominal operating voltage of 6 volts have a minimum operating voltage of about 4.7 or 4.8 volts, and this makes them just about suitable for operation on a nominal 5 volt supply. The coil resistance is an important factor to keep in mind, and in general, the higher this resistance the better. A high resistance has the advantage of giving a relatively low level of current consumption (the current drain is equal to the supply voltage divided by the coil resistance). A 12 volt type with a 1200 ohm coil would therefore have a current consumption of only around 10 milliamps (0.01 amps), but a 12 volt 120 ohm coil would take some 100 milliamps (0.1 amps). This factor is especially important where a circuit has several relays, as types having a low coil resistance could result in the circuit drawing a massive supply current under worst case conditions (with all the relays switched on). It is generally easier to locate suitable medium – high resistance relays than to provide the system with a large and expensive power supply. The BC547 specified for Tr1 can handle supply currents of up to 100 milliamps, and it should not be necessary to have higher currents than this although it could be changed for a higher current type (such as the 500 milliamp BC337) if necessary. The 30 volt maximum supply voltage is imposed by the maximum collector to emitter voltage rating of Tr1, but again, this should be more than adequate.

There are some reed relays available which can either be driven directly from a computer port or which can be driven reliably from a 5 volt supply via a relay driver, but these usually only have very low contact ratings, especially when used with inductive loads, and this makes them unsuitable for our purposes.

The relay provides a mechanical switching action of some kind, and there are two basic types. These are the straightforward on/off type, and changeover contacts. Most relays these days seem to have changeover contacts, and this is sensible as these can replace simple on/off types, but the latter can not be used in place of changeover contacts. Some relays only have one set of contacts, but most types have two or four sets. For straightforward on/off switching of an electric motor the simple set up of Figure 3 is all that is needed. The relay contacts are shown as changeover types with one terminal ignored so that the required on/off switching action is obtained. This is the way you will most probably need to do things, but obviously a set of true on/off contacts could be used instead.

For basic train control it is not just on/off switching that is required, and direction control is also needed. To alter the direction of the motor it is merely necessary to reverse the supply

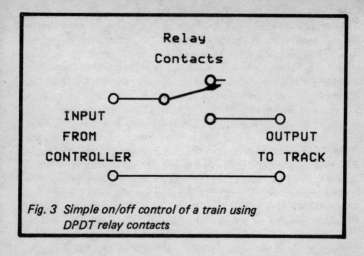

Fig. 3 Simple on/off control of a train using DPDT relay contacts

polarity, and this can be achieved using twin changeover contacts in the arrangement shown in Figure 4. Note that it is not possible to use a single relay for both on/off and direction control, and that two relays controlled from separate output lines are required.

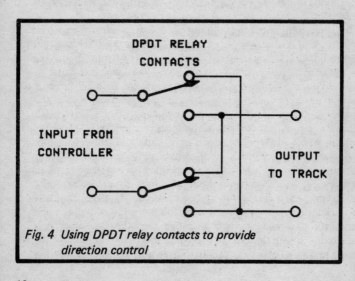

Fig. 4 Using DPDT relay contacts to provide direction control

Components for Simple Relay Driver (Fig. 2)
Resistors (all ¼ watt 5%)
R1   2k2
R2   3k9

Semiconductors
D1   1N4148
Tr1   BC547

Semiconductor Control
Controlling a motor via relays has the advantages of complete isolation between the controlling circuit and the motor, it is a rugged method of switching which is not easily damaged, and is extremely simple. The big drawback in train controller applications is that it only provides straightforward on/off switching with no speed control. This only permits rather crude control of trains with what are at best, very unrealistic results. Relay control is a good starting point for someone who is new to electronics, and relays are useful for the control of other devices (lighting for example), but otherwise a more sophisticated method of control is preferable. One way in which relay control is very valuable in a train controller application is to provide direction control. This can be achieved using semiconductor switches, but a relay usually represents a cheaper and easier way of doing things.

It is possible to drive the motor via a simple transistor switch, rather like a relay driver but designed to handle the higher powers involved. This can lead to problems in a train controller application though, due to problems with earthing. It is better to use a somewhat more complex arrangement such as the one shown in the circuit diagram of Figure 5, where one side of the motor connects to earth (the negative supply rail). This circuit also has a slight refinement in the form of a simple C – R delay circuit which prevents the train from simply skidding to a halt when the computer sends a stop signal, and rocketing straight off at full speed when it sends a start signal. This enables control of the train to be achieved using simple on/off commands from the computer, but it gives reasonably realistic results. Being basically a constant voltage type controller, results tend to be better when the train is steadily brought to a halt than they are when it is started, and with this type of controller there is a tendency for the train to do a so-called jump start. There is no really easy solution

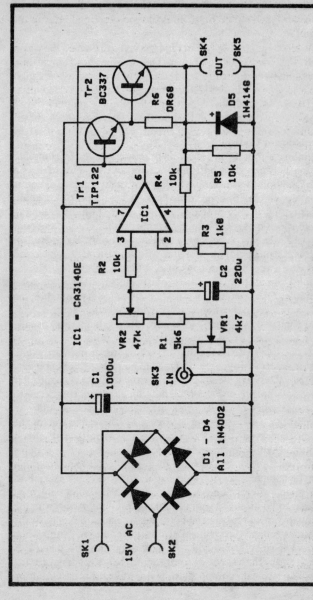

Fig. 5 The circuit diagram of the automatic ramping controller

12

to this problem, and it requires the use of a more sophisticated controller (such as the pulse control type described later in this chapter).

The block diagram shown in Figure 6 helps to explain the way in which the controller operates. The rectifier and smoothing circuits are used to produce a reasonably low ripple DC supply from a 15 volt AC input. The unit can also be powered from a 12 volt DC input, but most train controllers/power supplies have a raw (only rectified and not smoothed) DC output which still requires the built-in smoothing circuit. With a DC power source the rectifier stage is not strictly necessary, but it is probably worthwhile leaving it in circuit as it effectively provides polarity reversal protection, and will prevent the controller from being damaged if the supply is connected with the wrong polarity. In fact, with the rectifier circuit included the polarity with which a DC power source is connected to the unit is irrelevant. The smoothing, incidentally, is needed to give a supply from which the controller will operate reliably. DC electric motors will operate perfectly well from a pulsing DC supply (but they will not operate at all from a true AC power source).

An amplifier is at the heart of the unit, and this is required because the input from the computer will only be in the region of 0 to 5 volts, whereas the output to the motor must be at around 0 to 15 volts or more. The voltage gain of this amplifier therefore boosts the drive signal to produce a suitably large output voltage range. A potentiometer at the input of the unit can be used to trim the maximum output voltage to the required figure. This is a very useful feature as it enables the maximum speed of the train to be set at whatever speed is desired, and if the controlled train is something like a goods train which is only required to go at a snails-pace, the unit can be set up to achieve this. Another reason for including this control is that the full smoothed DC output might be too high for some engines, and this control can then be backed off to give an acceptable maximum output for the motor concerned.

The delay circuit is placed between the speed control and the amplifier, and it is just a simple C – R timing circuit which gives an exponential ramp signal at the output as the train is started and stopped. In other words, as the output voltage rises, it does so at a fairly high initial rate, and gradually slows down as maximum output voltage is approached. As the output voltage decreases, the initial rate of fall is high, but it steadily diminishes as the

13

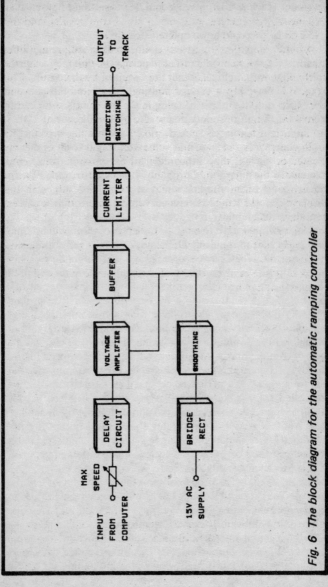

Fig. 6 The block diagram for the automatic ramping controller

14

output approaches zero. It would be possible to include circuitry to give a linear rate of increase and decrease, but in practice an exponential characteristic seems to give better results, and this extra circuitry would be completely pointless.

A buffer amplifier is used at the output of the voltage amplifier stage, and this is needed in order to permit the unit to provide the fairly high output currents that are required by the motor. This stage is followed by a current limiting circuit, and this prevents very high output currents flowing in the event of a short circuit across the output or some other severe overload occuring. This is an important feature as such overloads are not uncommon with train controllers, and without some very rapid form of current limiter or cutout, the output device (and possibly other components in the unit) would probably soon be destroyed. Fuses or electro-mechanical cutouts would probably not suffice in this application, and would be less convenient in use than a current limiting circuit anyway.

The final stage of the unit is the direction control switch. This is not really part of the controller proper, and is a relay and driver circuit of the type described previously. The direction switching must be at the output of the unit, and not at the front end of the unit (where it would have no effect).

Components for Automatic Ramping Controller (Fig. 5)
Resistors (all ¼ watt 5% except where noted)

R1	5k6
R2	10k
R3	1k8
R4	10k
R5	10k
R6	0R68 1W

Potentiometers

VR1	4k7 lin
VR2	47k lin

Capacitors

C1	1000µ 25V electrolytic
C2	220µ 10V electrolytic

Semiconductors

IC1	CA3140E
Tr1	TIP122
Tr2	BC337
D1 to D4	1N4002 (4 off)
D5	1N4148

Miscellaneous

| SK1, 2, 4, 5 | 4mm sockets (4 off) |
| SK3 | Phono socket |

Metal instrument case
Circuit board
8 pin DIL IC holder
Insulating kit for Tr1
Two control knobs
Wire, solder, etc.

Circuit Operation

If we return now to the circuit diagram of Figure 5, D1 to D4 are the bridge rectifier which converts the 15 volt AC Supply into a fullwave rectified DC output. Note that the unit must be powered from the mains supply only via a suitable step-down and isolation transformer, and that it would be extremely dangerous to attempt to power the unit from the mains supply in any other way. C1 is the smoothing capacitor, and it gives a reasonably well smoothed output, although there is still a significant amount of ripple present on the supply. This does not adversely affect the performance of the unit though.

The amplifier is based on IC1 which is an operational amplifier connected in the non-inverting mode. A slightly unusual aspect of the circuit is that it is an operational amplifier connected as a DC amplifier, but only a single supply is used rather than the dual balanced types that would be more normal for this type of circuit. It is possible to do this for two reasons. One is simply that the output only ever needs to be positive, and will never be negative. The other is that IC1 is a device which will work properly with its inputs and output at voltages almost right down to the 0 volt supply potential. Few other devices can achieve this, and devices such as the 741C and LF351 will not work properly in this circuit. In fact they will fail to work at all, and will simply give something in the region of maximum output regardless of the input signal level. The voltage gain of the amplifier is about 6.5 times, which

16

should be more than adequate, but if necessary R4 can be made slightly higher in value in order to give more gain.

VR1 is the maximum speed control, and this is just a volume control style variable attenuator used to process the input signal from the computer. The delay circuit is a straightforward C – R type having R1 as the resistive element and C2 as the capacitive element. VR2 enables the time taken for the output to reach maximum (or fall from maximum to zero) to be adjusted from a little over one second to about 10 seconds or so. It would be possible to have the start and stop times individually adjustable, although this is not quite as easy as one might think. However, in practice there seems to be little advantage (if any) in doing this, and it was not included in the final design. R2 is a protection resistor for IC1.

Turning to the output side of IC1, Tr1 is the buffer amplifier and this is an emitter follower stage. The TIP122 specified for Tr1 is actually a power Darlington device, and this provides the very high current gain needed in order to enable IC1 to provide outputs currents of up to about 1 amp with minimal voltage drop under loading. The minimum current gain of the TIP122 is some 5000 in fact, and it should not be replaced with an ordinary power transistor which would probably have a current gain of only about one hundredth of this figure.

R6 and Tr2 form the current limiting circuit, and they operate in a conventional arrangement which is well tried and tested, and very reliable. With output currents of less than about 1 amp the voltage produced across R6 is too low to switch on Tr2, and the latter consequently has no effect on the circuit. At higher currents though, the voltage across R6 reaches about 0.65 volts or so, and Tr2 switches on to some degree. This results in it tapping off some of the output current from IC1 and pulling the output voltage lower.

The higher the output current that is drawn, the greater the voltage that is developed across R6, the harder Tr2 is taken into conduction, and the lower the output voltage is taken. The practical effect of this is to reduce the output voltage to a level which allows an output current of little more than 1 amp to flow. Even with a short circuit on the output, the current flow will be little more than an amp as the output voltage would be reduced to practically zero. The current limiting is very quick acting, and is certainly fast enough in operation to prevent overloads from damaging Tr1.

R5 is just a load resistor for Tr1, and D5 is a protection diode which prevents any reverse voltage spikes generated across the electric motor from damaging any of the semiconductor devices in the circuit. In practice the output of the circuit is connected to the tracks via a set of DPDT relay contacts which provide direction control, as mentioned previously. The relay can be powered from the controller, with the supply being taken from across C1. The unloaded supply voltage is typically a little over 20 volts, but will normally fall to well under 20 volts under load. This is rather higher than that recommended for most 12 volt relays, but the easy solution to the problem is to add a 1 watt resistor having a value equal to about 60% of the relay's coil resistance in series with the relay coil. Of course, if manual control of the train's direction is acceptable, then the relay contacts could be replaced with a DPDT switch.

Construction
Construction of the unit raises few problems, and it can easily be built on stripboard, or the printed circuit layout of Figure 7 (copper track) and Figure 8 (component layout) can be used. Whatever the method of construction, bear in mind that IC1 has a PMOS input stage and that it consequently requires the normal antistatic handling precautions to be observed. Use an 8 pin DIL integrated circuit holder for this device, and do not plug it into circuit until construction of the unit is in other respects complete. The CA3140E should be supplied in some form of antistatic packaging, which is normally a plastic tube or conductive foam. Leave it in this packaging until it is time to plug it into the holder, and handle the device as little as possible. Keep the device away from any obvious sources of static electricity when handling it.

Tr1 will dissipate several watts under certain operating conditions, and it will overheat and be destroyed unless it is fitted with an adequate heatsink. One way of tackling things is to mount it off-board on a medium size (about 4.5 degrees Centigrade per watt) ready made heatsink, or if a metal case is used it will probably be possible to mount it somewhere on this so that the case acts as the heatsink. A third alternative is to mount Tr1 on the board, and to fabricate a bracket from 16 or 18 s.w.g. aluminium to conduct heat from the device and carry it into the case. This bracket can also act as part of the mounting for the board. This third method represents the most difficult one, but it gives the

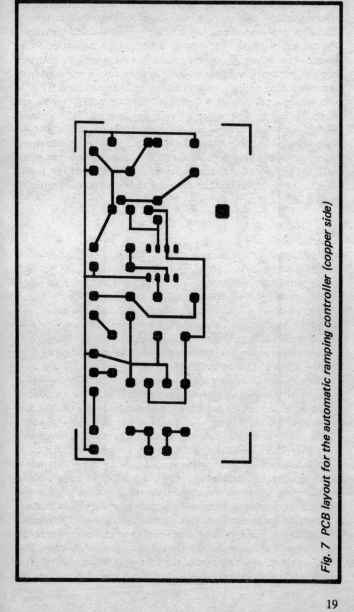

Fig. 7 PCB layout for the automatic ramping controller (copper side)

19

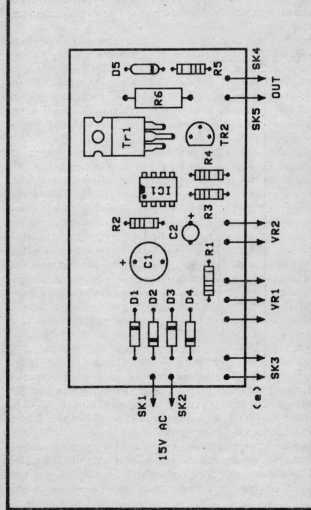

Fig. 8 The component overlay for the automatic ramping controller

20

neatest and strongest finished article, and is my preferred way of doing things.

Note that Tr1's heat tab connects internally to its collector leadout wire. It should therefore be mounted using the standard insulating washer and plastic bush so that the case does not connect to the positive supply rail by way of Tr1 (which might not be fatal to the circuit, but would certainly be an undesirable state of affairs).

The types of socket specified in the components list are only suggestions, and these should be changed to any type which would be more convenient in your particular set up. R6 is specified as a 1 watt 0.68 ohm resistor, but a suitable component may be difficult to locate. It might be necessary to use a higher wattage component in order to obtain one of the correct value, or another solution would be to use two half watt resistors of 1.2 ohms and 1.5 ohms wired in parallel.

There should be no difficulty in powering the unit from the 15 volt AC output of a train controller, or if desired the unit can have a built-in 15 volt mains transformer to provide its power. However, the normal safety precautions would have to be observed, and any exposed metalwork would have to be earthed to the mains earth lead. It is probably best to use a metal case and then to earth this to the mains earth lead (along with the negative supply rail). Anything metal which is mounted on the case is then automatically earthed properly. The case should be a type with a screw fixing lid or cover so that easy access to the dangerous mains wiring is not possible. Ideally, any connections carrying the mains supply should be insulated with sleeving or insulating "boots". Any mains transformer having a voltage rating in the range 12 to 15 volts and a current rating of 1.4 amps or more should be suitable as the power source for this project.

If the unit is powered from a 12 volt DC output of a controller there is a slight risk of earthing problems, although in most cases both output terminals will be isolated from earth and no difficulties should arise. If in any doubt about this it would be advisable to power the unit only from a 15 volt AC output or from its own built-in mains transformer.

From the software point of view the unit is very easy to control. For example, assume that the controller is fed from PB0 of the BBC computer's user port, and that PB1 is used for direction control. This gives four possible sets of output states, as follows:-

User Port Value	Effect
0	Forward, train stopped
1	Forward, train powered
2	Reverse, train stopped
3	Reverse, train powered

In reality there are only three actions obtained, since the direction setting is obviously irrelevant if the train is stopped. The most basic type of software would have three keys of the computer's keyboard monitored by a software loop, with a value of 0, 1, or 3 being sent to the user port depending on which key was the last to be operated. In other words the three keys would act as stop, forward, and reverse controls. An alternative would be a very basic form of fully automatic operation where the train goes in one direction for a certain period of time, then stops for a certain length of time, then goes in the reverse direction, or whatever action you desire.

This is admittedly only a very basic form of control, whether you choose manual or automatic operation, but it is useful for checking the controller and as a simple exercise in writing control sofware. In order to get the most from the controller you will need some form of sensor (or several sensors) so that the computer can roughly follow the train's progress along or around the track. It is then possible to have the train stop at some particular point on the track, to program the computer to make the train do a certain number of laps around the track, and this sort of thing. Sensors are a subject that will be dealt with in the next chapter.

Speed Control
In order to give maximum versatility and the most realistic results it is necessary to have fairly precise control over the train's speed, and not just simple on/off switching. There are a number of possible ways of obtaining speed control via a computer, and we will consider three of them here.

The most obvious method of control is to have a controller of the constant voltage type, but with the controlling voltage provided by the computer via a digital to analogue converter, rather than by way of a manually controlled potentiometer. This gives a set up of the type outlined in the block diagram of Figure 9.

Speed control, by this means at any rate, requires the use of more than one output from the computer, and the more speeds that are required, the greater the number of output lines that must

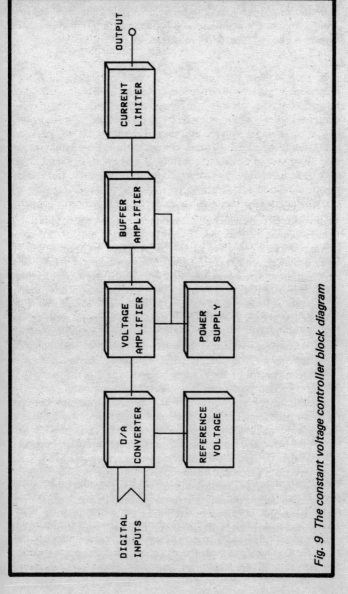

Fig. 9 The constant voltage controller block diagram

be used. The table that follows shows the relationship between the number of output lines and the number of speeds provided (the real number of available speeds is one less than shown since one speed is needed as an "off" setting).

Output Lines	Speeds
1	2
2	4
3	8
4	16
5	32
6	64
7	128
8	256

It is possible to produce very inexpensive digital to analogue converter circuits which require only about three input lines, but these obviously give only a limited range of speeds. To some extent the lack of speeds can be compensated for by using a C – R smoothing circuit to prevent any sudden switches from one speed to another and thus give more realistic results. However, having a full range of speeds available gives greater versatility, and is probably well worthwhile the small additional expense involved.

The 256 speeds available from a full 8 bit output is more than is really necessary, and this would give no noticeable change in speed from one to the next. It would also have the disadvantage of not leaving any output lines free for other purposes, such as direction control or for reading sensors, making it necessary to have a second port even for a fairly basic computer controlled system. Just what represents the best compromise between economy of lines used and the number of speeds available is to some extent a subjective one, but five or six bits give good control over the train, and leave two or three lines free for other purposes. With the design featured here you can choose your own compromise, which can be anything from 1 to 8 bits.

The digital to analogue converter is a fairly complex device, and a detailed description of its operation would be out of place here, but its main constituents are eight electronic switches (one operated from each digital input) and a complex resistor network fed from a reference voltage. In this application a highly stable reference source is not really necessary, since any slight variations in the output voltage due to temperature changes (or whatever) are unlikely to produce any noticeable effect on results. A highly stable reference source is used in this design merely because it is a feature of the digital to analogue converter chip, and there is no point in not using it.

Just how the values sent to the converter relate to the actual output voltages produced depends on the design of the particular converter concerned. The maximum output voltage is equal to the potential provided by the reference voltage source, or 2.55 volts in this case. This gives a range of output voltages from 0 to 2.55 volts in 10 millivolt (0.01 volt) increments if all eight inputs are utilized. It is not essential to use all eight inputs though, and for lower resolution the least significant bit or bits can simply be wired to ground. As an example, with bits 0 and 1 tied to earth, the converter would provide a range of 64 output voltages from 0 to 2.52 volts in 40 millivolt (0.04 volt) steps.

Not utilizing all the available inputs reduces the maximum output voltage available, although not by a large enough margin to be of any real significance. The output voltage range of the circuit is insufficient to drive the electric motor of a model train anyway, and the digital to analogue converter is therefore followed by a voltage amplifier. This is in turn followed by a buffer stage which provides the high output current needed in this application. Finally, a current limiting circuit protects the unit against short circuits or other overloads on the output. A simple unregulated power supply provides power for the voltage amplifier and buffer stages, but the digital to analogue converter requires a stable and well smoothed supply, and it is powered from the computer.

Converter Circuit

Figure 10 shows the circuit diagram of the digital to analogue converter, and this is based on the Ferranti ZN426E device. This contains virtually all the components needed for an accurate 8 bit converter, and as will be apparent from Figure 10, very few discrete components are required.

Of the few discrete components that are required, R1 is the load resistor for the internal 2.55 volt shunt regulator, and C1 decouples any noise on the output of this circuit. C2 is merely a supply decoupling capacitor. The unit is powered from the +5 volt supply output of the computer, and virtually every computer can provide a suitable power source (I have yet to come across a home computer which does not have a +5 volt supply output). The

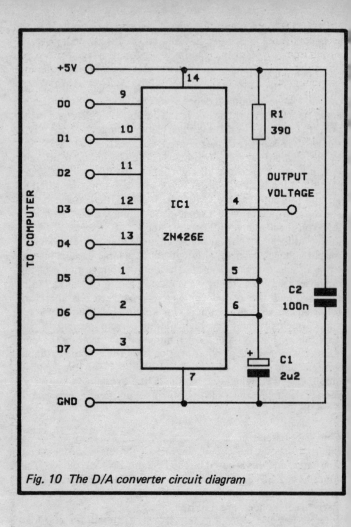

Fig. 10 The D/A converter circuit diagram

ZN426E is a low current device, and its modest power requirements should not put any strain on the computer's power supply.

Although Figure 10 shows all eight inputs of IC1 as being used, as explained earlier, it is best to only use five or six of its inputs. The unused inputs should be the least significant ones (inputs

"D0", "D1", etc.), and they should be wired to earth. I would suggest the use of just five bits, but you might like to try the unit using from (say) four to eight bits to determine which number you consider to be the best compromise. Of course, if your computer system provides plenty of digital outputs then you may prefer to use all eight bits.

Assuming that you use less than the full eight inputs, it is probably best to drive the unit from the least significant lines of the computer's parallel output port. This may seem an odd way of doing things, as it results in the least significant outputs of the computer driving the most significant inputs of the converter. Figure 11 shows the arrangement that would be used with a five bit system, and this clearly shows what I mean. The point of using this method of driving the circuit is that the speed of the train with (say) a five bit system is controlled by writing values in the range 0 to 31 to the output port. Things are not actually as straightforward as this since the three most significant lines (or some of them) will presumably be used as outputs to control the direction of the train or something of this nature, and the values written to the port

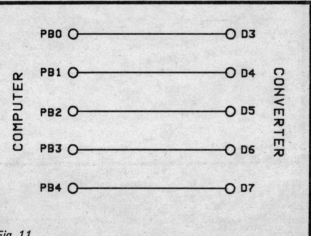

Fig. 11
This method of connecting the converter to the computer may look odd but it is the most convenient method

must be modified to take this into account. Even so, it is generally much more convenient to have the range of values to control the train's speed as something like 0 to 31, rather than something like even numbers from 0 to 62 (which would be the result if the unit was driven from bits D1 to D6).

Components for Constant Voltage Controller (Figs. 10, 12 & 13)
Resistors (all ¼ watt 5% unless noted)

R1	390
R2	4k7
R3	0.68 ohms (1 watt)
R4	10k

Potentiometer

VR1	47k hor sub-min preset

Capacitors

C1	2μ2 63V elect
C2	100n ceramic
C3	1000μ 25V elect
C4	100n ceramic
C5	100n ceramic

Semiconductors

IC1	ZN426E
IC2	CA3140E
IC3	μA7805
D1	1N4148
D2 to D5	1N4002 (4 off)
Tr1	TIP122
Tr2	BC337

Miscellaneous

S1	Rotary mains switch
T1	Mains primary, 15 volt 1.5A secondary
FS1	20mm 1A quick-blow
SK1,SK2	4 mm socket (2 off)

Metal instrument case
Circuit board
8 pin DIL IC holder
14 pin DIL IC holder

Heatsink (see text)
Mains plug and lead, wire, solder, etc.

N.B. C4, C5, and IC3 are only needed if a 5 volt supply for the
converter is not available from the computer.

Component for Pulsed Controller (Figs. 10, 17, 18, 19)
Resistors (all ¼ watt 5%)

R1	390
R2	2k2
R3	1k
R4	10k
R5	10k
R6	10k
R7	15k
R8	5k6
R9	5k6
R10	100k
R11	100k

Potentiometer

VR1	1k hor sub-min preset

Capacitors

C1	2µ2 63V elect
C2	100n ceramic
C3	68n polyester
C4	100µ 25V elect
C5	2200µ 25V elect
C6 to C9	100n ceramic (4 off)

Semiconductors

IC1	ZN426E
IC2	CA3240E
IC3	LM358
IC4	µA7805
IC5	µA7815
D1	1N4148
D2 to D5	1N4002 (4 off)
Tr1	TIP122

Miscellaneous

FS1	20mm 1A quick-blow
SK1, SK2	4mm socket (2 off)
T1	Mains primary, 15 volt 1.5 amp secondary

Metal instrument case
Circuit board
8 pin DIL IC holder (2 off)
14 pin DIL IC holder
20mm fuseholder
Mains plug and lead, wire, solder, etc.

N.B.
IC4, C6, and C8 are not needed if the computer can supply a
5 volt output for the D/A converter circuit

Controller Circuit

The main circuit of the controller is shown in Figure 12, and this is
the amplifier, output buffer and current limiter stages. There is
little point in giving a detailed description of this circuit as is is

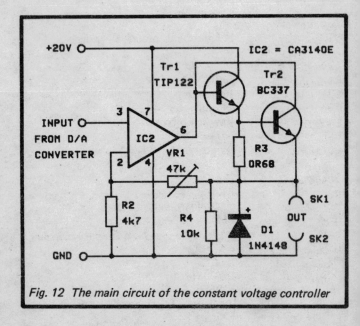

Fig. 12 The main circuit of the constant voltage controller

essentially the same as the corresponding stages of the automatic ramping controller circuit (Figure 5) which was described previously. The only difference is that there is no potentiometer at the input to permit the input voltage to be adjusted to give the desired output voltage swing. Instead, VR1 is included in the negative feedback circuit of the amplifier, and this enables the voltage gain to be varied from unity at minimum resistance to nominally eleven times at maximum resistance. This enables the maximum output voltage to be adjusted to anything from about 2.5 volts to the maximum that the supply voltage will support (which is typically around 20 volts under no load).

Components for Pulsed Controller (software driven)
(Figs. 12 and 13)
Resistors (all ¼ watt 5% unless noted)
R2   4k7
R3   0.68 ohms (1 watt)
R4   10k

Potentiometer
VR1   47k sub-min hor preset

Capacitor
C3 1000μ 25V elect

Semiconductors
IC2   *CA3140E*
D1   *1N4148*
D2 to D5   *1N4002 (4 off)*
Tr1   *TIP122*
Tr2   *BC337*

Miscellaneous
S1   Rotary mains switch
FS1   20mm 1 amp quick-blow
SK1, SK2   4mm socket (2 off)
T1   Mains primary, 15 volt 1.5 amp secondary
Metal instrument case
Circuit board
8 pin DIL IC holder
20mm fuseholder
Mains plug and lead, wire, solder, etc.

N.B. IC3, C4, and C5 of Fig.13 and the components of Fig.10 are not needed

PSU Circuit

Figure 13 shows the full circuit diagram of the mains power supply. It is assumed here that the unit will be contructed as a self contained unit with a built-in mains transformer. However, if preferred, T1 and S1 can be omitted, and the bridge rectifier (D2 to D5) can be fed from the 15 volt AC output of an existing train controller. The 15 volt AC supply, however it is derived, is fullwave rectified by D2 to D5 and then smoothed by C3 to give an unloaded DC output of around 20 volts or so.

IC3 is a 5 volt monolithic voltage regulator which provides a +5 volt rail for the digital to analogue converter circuit. As explained earlier, most computers will have a 5 volt output which can be used to power the converter circuit, but if a suitable supply output is not available this simple regulator circuit will provide an alternative. The low power μA78L05 device could be used in the IC3 position as the current drawn by the converter circuit is well within the 100 milliamp maximum for this device even under worst case conditions. There is a minor problem though, in that the relatively high voltage across the device could result in it having an excessive level of power dissipation. This could be overcome by adding a dropper resistor in series with the input to the device, but it is probably cheaper and easier just to use the standard μA7805 device (which will not need a heatsink).

Pulse Control

While the constant voltage type of controller gives reasonably good results, it is less than perfect. As pointed out earlier, there is a tendency for the train to not move at first, and to then suddenly move off at a fairly high rate, instead of moving off slowly and steadily accelerating away. Speed regulation at slow speeds is also less than perfect with the train tending to run away slightly as it goes down gradients, and of more importance, tending to stall as it climbs gradients.

One way of obtaining better regulation is to use an over-compensated voltage regulator circuit, so that the voltage fed to the motor actually increases slightly under heavier loading, and decreases slightly under reduced loading. This type of speed regulator can work very efficiently indeed, and is much used in

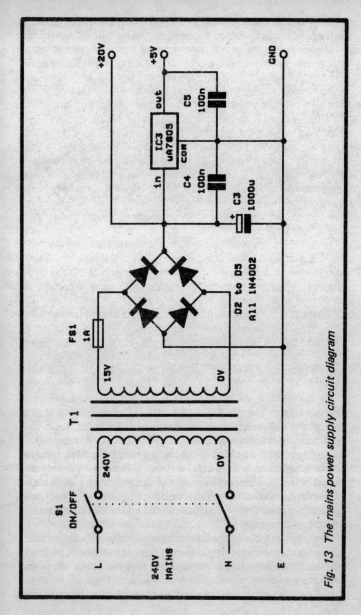

Fig. 13 The mains power supply circuit diagram

33

critical applications such as speed control of motors in cassette recorders. It works best in applications where only a single speed is required, and the circuit is designed to accurately complement the characteristics of the motor. It could no doubt be made to work well in a train controller application, but it is probably much easier to use a pulsed controller circuit. This is a totally different concept, but one which works very well in this application.

With a pulsed controller, as its name would suggest, the output signal is a series of pulses rather than a steady DC signal. Provided the frequency of the pulses is within acceptable limits, this type of supply will give perfectly good results when used with an ordinary DC electric motor. The pulse frequency must not be too low (less than aound 30Hz) or the effect would be much the same as rapidly switching an ordinary controller on and off by hand, with the train tending to move along in a series of short jumps, giving very unrealistic results.

If the frequency is made too high, the impedance of the coils in the electric motor would be very high at the signal frequency, resulting in no significant current flow. The result of this would be a very slow maximum speed, if the train could actually be induced to start at all.

There is a fairly wide latitude as far as the output frequency is concerned, and in practice anything from 100Hz or a little less to around 1kHz (1000Hz) or even more will give good results. In my experience with various pulsed controllers and engines, somewhere in the region of 200Hz to 250Hz gives about optimum results.

The amount of power fed to the motor is controlled by varying the mark-space ratio of the output signal. The waveforms shown in Figure 14 help to explain how this system operates.

In the waveform of Figure 14(a) the output signal is a squarewave with a perfect 1 to 1 mark-space ratio. This gives an average output voltage equal to half the peak output voltage, and the train would therefore be driven at half power. In Figure 14(b) the output pulses have been lengthened so that each one only finishes just before the next one commences. The output is therefore at its peak value for the vast majority of the time, and the average output voltage is only slightly less than the peak value. The train is therefore driven at very nearly full power. With some pulsed controllers the output signal is always a series of pulses, and full power is never quite reached. This is of no practical consequence though, as the power loss caused by the very brief

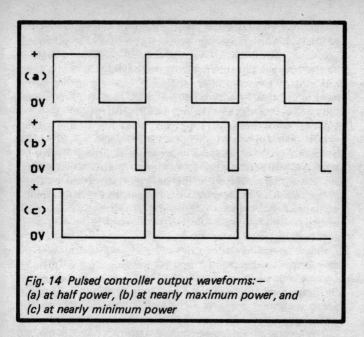

Fig. 14 Pulsed controller output waveforms:—
(a) at half power, (b) at nearly maximum power, and
(c) at nearly minimum power

gap between pulses is far too low to be noticeable in normal use. With some designs the output does cease to be a pulse train at maximum power, with the output going permanently high.

Figure 14(c) shows the output waveform at almost minimum power. Here the output pulses are very short with relatively long periods separating them, and the average output voltage is very low. With some pulsed controllers there are output pulses even at minimum output power, but they are so brief that the power fed to the train is far too low to result in it moving (there may be a slight audible "hum" from the motor though). With other pulsed controller designs the output does fully cut off at minimum power, with no output pulses being produced.

This may seem like a clever way of achieving results that are no different to those obtained with a constant voltage type controller, but there are actually two distinct advantages to the pulsed output approach. The one of greatest importance is the improved starting and low speed performance that it imparts. The type of motor used in model trains has a reluctance to start, and it is this factor which gives the jump start effect. The voltage applied to the motor has to be sufficient to drive the motor at medium speed in order to get it to start, and once it has started it immediately jumps to this medium speed. It is the same effect that gives the motor a tendency to stall when it is running at low speeds. If increased loading should cause the motor to momentarily falter, once stopped it takes a substantial increase in power before it will start up again.

With manual control a skilled operator can use some deft manipulation of the speed control in order to compensate for these short-comings to some extent, but with computer control there is no easy equivalent to this. It would be possible to use sensors and a feedback system to overcome the problems, but it is more practical to use a controller with better control characteristics. The pulsed type controller achieves this by effectively applying full power to the motor for short periods of time. These high power pulses resist any tendency for the motor to stall, and help to spur it into operation if increased loading (or dirty tracks) cause the train to momentarily falter. This is not all purely theoretical, and the improvement in starting performance and low speed regulation between a constant voltage controller and a pulsed type is something which is very obvious in use.

The second advantage of a pulsed controller is that the output device is either switched hard on, or is switched fully off. This helps to keep down the amount of power dissipated in the device since there is very little voltage across the component when it is switched on, and although the current flow is likely to be quite large, the power dissipated by the device (which is equal to the voltage across it multiplied by the current flow) is likely to be quite modest. When the output device is switched off the current flow is reduced to just minute leakage currents, and although the voltage across the component is then quite high, the power it dissipates is negligible.

The practical result of this is that the output transistor stays quite cool with the aid of little or no heatsinking, which helps to keep down the cost of the controller as well as making things much more straightforward from the constructional point of view.

Software Approach

There is more than one way of generating the output waveforms for pulsed control, and one way of tackling things is to use a software approach. This has the advantage of needing only a fairly

36

simple hardware interface, and really all that is needed is a circuit of the type shown in Figure 12 (and described previously). Instead of being driven from the digital to analogue converter circuit, this would be driven from a digital output of the computer. Software routines would then be used to generate the appropriate waveforms, with the interface providing the necessary voltage and current amplification to enable an electric motor to be driven properly. Of course, the mains power supply circuit of Figure 13 is also needed, but the 5 volt regulator section of this would not.

Although this system is very simple from the hardware point of view, it is more than a little awkward as far as the software side of things is concerned. Although the output frequency does not need to be particularly high, accurate control of the output pulse duration and spacing is essential, and can not be achieved using even a fast version of BASIC. Machine code or assembly language routines are really required in this application, and it is consequently something that should only be undertaken by a fairly experienced programmer. There are various ways of tackling the problem, but probably the best way is to use separate timing loops to set the high and low periods of the output waveform. In its simplest form this just entails having a preset time for the high output period, and using a variable time to spread these out or to compact them, so as to give a low or high average output voltage respectively. This can work quite well, although it gives variations in output frequency, and care has to be taken to keep the output frequency within acceptable limits. A better but slightly more difficult approach, is to vary both the high and low output periods, with an increase in one being accompanied by a complementary decrease in the other. This keeps the output frequency constant, or very nearly so, and provided a suitable frequency is selected, it ensures that good results are always obtained.

I can not claim to be a great supporter of this way of doing things, and much prefer to use slightly more complicated hardware which enables sophisticated control to be achieved using relatively simple software. This admittedly involves higher building costs, but it is still a much more practical approach unless you are fully competent at machine code or assembly language programming. Another point to bear in mind is that home computers have limited processing power, and with software being used to directly generate the output waveforms there is danger that this is all the computer would be able to do, with insufficient processing time being left for monitoring sensors or other purposes.

Those who have sufficient programming knowledge should have no difficulty in persuing this method of control, but it is something that will not be considered further here.

Controller Operation

There are numerous harware approaches to pulsed speed control, but the standard approach uses a system along the lines of the block diagram shown in Figure 15, and this is a method which offers excellent results while not requiring anything particularly exotic or expensive in terms of the hardware.

The basic pulse signal is generated by the clock oscillator and voltage comparator stages. The voltage comparator sets its output high or low depending on whether the clock signal is higher or lower in voltage than a reference voltage. This reference voltage is the control voltage in this case, and it is provided by the computer via a digital to analogue converter circuit. The clock signal is a triangular waveform, and on peaks it provides a higher voltage than the reference voltage, sending the output of the voltage comparator high. At what point on each cycle the output of the comparator triggers to the high state, and where it returns to the low state, depends on the reference voltage, and this gives the required conversion from a steady DC signal to a pulsed signal.

Figure 16 helps to demonstate how this conversion is achieved. In Figure 16(a) the bias voltage has been set exactly half way between the minimum and maximum voltages of the clock signal, and this gives a squarewave output signal with a 1 to 1 mark-space ratio. The bias voltage has been set higher in Figure 16(b), so that the output of the voltage comparator only triggers to the high state on peaks of the clock signal, giving a lower average output voltage from the comparator. Finally, in Figure 16(c) the reference voltage has been set at a low level, so that the clock signal is at a higher voltage for the majority of the time, and a high average output voltage is obtained from the comparator.

With the arrangement described above the system provides a pulsed output voltage that can be varied from zero to the full supply voltage by means of a DC control voltage, but high input voltages give low output potentials, and vice versa. This inversion does not actually matter, provided the software is written to take into account that high output values give low speeds, and low output values give high speeds. In practice the inversion can be

38

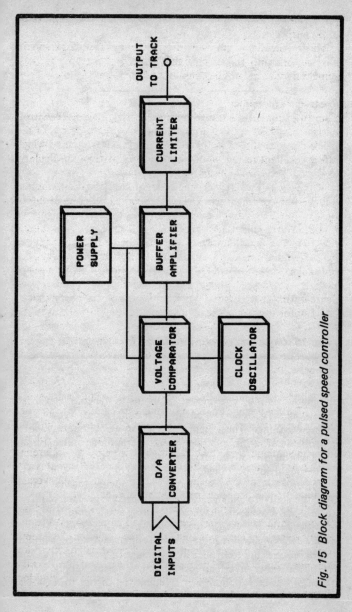

Fig. 15 Block diagram for a pulsed speed controller

39

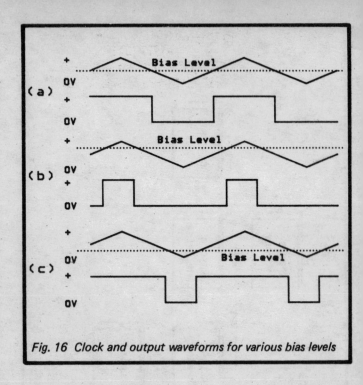

Fig. 16 Clock and output waveforms for various bias levels

eliminated simply by reversing the inputs to the comparator, so that its output goes high when the clock signal goes lower than the reference voltage. The system works just as well either way, but it is probably easier to use this second method of connection, as when writing the software it is easier to think in terms of the speed being roughly proportional to the values sent to the output port.

Returning now to the block diagram of Figure 15, the voltage from the digital to analogue converter is used to give the required pulse signal from the voltage comparator, and a buffer amplifier provides a current boost so that the low impedance load presented by the electric motor can be driven properly. A current limiter circuit protects the controller from damage in the event of a short circuit or other overload occuring. A power supply circuit provides power for the unit, including the digital to analogue converter if necessary.

Circuit Operation

The digital to analogue converter circuit of Figure 10 (and described earlier) is also used in this pulsed controller design, and requires no modification whatever. Just the same as when it is used in the constant voltage controller design, it does not have to be used with all eight inputs driven from the computer, and five or six bit operation will provide good results.

Figure 17 shows the circuit diagram of the voltage comparator and output stages, while the clock oscillator and power supply circuits are shown separately in Figures 18 and 19 respectively.

Taking the main circuit of Figure 17 first, IC2b is an operational amplifier which operates here as the voltage comparator. Its non-inverting input is fed from the output of the digital to analogue converter circuit (Figure 10), while the inverting input is fed with the clock signal. However, in order to give good results the clock signal must stay within the same voltage limits as the control voltage from the digital to analogue converter, or between about 0 and +2.5 volts in other words. If the clock signal is outside these limits, proper control from zero to full speed will not be attainable.

The clock oscillator generates a signal having a peak-to-peak value of between 2 and 2.5 volts, but it is at a range of voltages centered on half the supply voltage. The clock oscillator could be biased to bring the output voltage range within the required limits, but this would result in distortion of the output waveform and proper operation of the unit would be upset.

A better way of doing things is to use a simple level shifter circuit to process the clock signal and bring it down to the required voltages, and this is the purpose of IC2a. This is really just an operational amplifier connected as a unity gain inverting mode amplifier. The inversion is of no consequence in this case as the clock signal is symmetrical. The bias voltage fed to IC2a's non-inverting input is reduced from its normal level of half the supply voltage so as to reduce the output voltage range of the amplifier, and VR1 is adjusted to give precisely the required output voltage range.

On the output side of IC2b, Tr1 is the buffer amplifier and this is a Darlington power device used in the common emitter mode. R6 is its load resistor and D1 is a protection diode. There is no current limiting circuit at the output of the unit, but such a circuit is unnecessary since current limiting is a feature of the power supply circuit, and Tr1 is therefore unable to draw an excessive supply current.

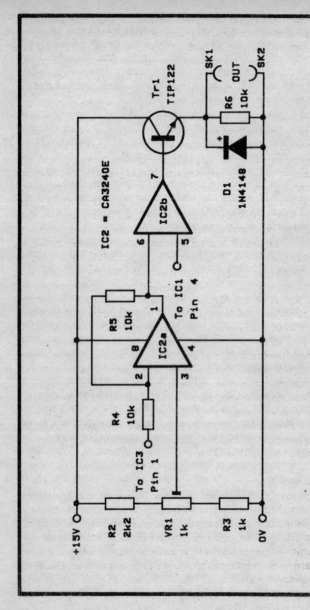

Fig. 17 The main circuit diagram of the pulse controller

42

The clock oscillator circuit of Figure 18 uses the standard squarewave/triangular wave generator configuration, with IC3a acting as the Miller Integrator, and IC3b operating as the Schmitt Trigger. In this case the squarewave output from IC3b is of no interest, and it is the high quality triangular signal from IC3a which is used as the clock signal. R10 and C3 are the timing components, and these set the operating frequency at typically just over 200Hz. As explained previously, this generally gives about optimum results, but if desired the operating frequency can be changed by altering the value of C3 (the output frequency is inversely proportional to the value of this component).

In the controller designs described previously in this book a non-stabilised supply has been used, but for good and consistent results this controller requires a reasonably stable and ripple-free supply at a potential of about 15 volts. This is provided by the circuit of Figure 19 which has T1 as the isolation and step- down transformer, D2 to D5 as a bridge rectifier which gives full wave rectification, and C5 as the smoothing capacitor. IC5 is a 15 volt monolithic voltage regulator which stabilises the output and gives electronic smoothing. IC5 incorporates current limiting, and this is of the "foldback" type. This is where a minor overload causes no significant increase in output current above the limiting threshold, as in normal current limiting, but a more severe overload actually produces a reduction in output current. In this case the current limiting commences at a nominal figure of 1 amp, and the short circuit output current is about 230 milliamps. This gives more comprehensive protection against overloads, and in particular reduces the risk of damage due to overloads that are maintained for some time.

IC4 is a 5 volt monolithic voltage regulator which provides a +5 volt supply output for the digital to analogue converter, if required.

Construction
These circuits can be used in three different configurations (constant voltage controller, software driven pulsed controller, and hardware implemented pulsed controller), but whichever of these is selected there should be no real difficulty as far as construction is concerned. The circuits are easily constructed on stripboard or it should not be too difficult to produce a custom printed circuit design.

A few points need to be borne in mind when building these

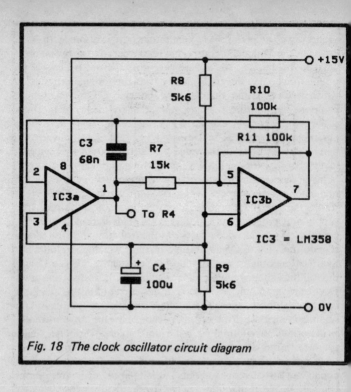

Fig. 18 The clock oscillator circuit diagram

controllers, and one of these is that the CA3140E and CA3240E integrated circuits are MOS types, and the standard antistatic handling precautions should be observed when dealing with these devices. None of the other semiconductors used in these designs are MOS types incidentally.

Heatsinks are also something that should be taken into consideration, and as already pointed out, Tr1 in the pulsed controller designs has to dissipate very little power and does not require a large heatsink. However, it is still advisable to fit this component with at least a small ready-made finned heatsink, or a home-made heatsink consisting of a small sheet of 16 swg aluminium bent into a 'U' shape. This will ensure that it operates at a reasonably low temperature so that good reliability is obtained. It also gives some degree of protection to the output transistor if a fault condition or output overload results in it

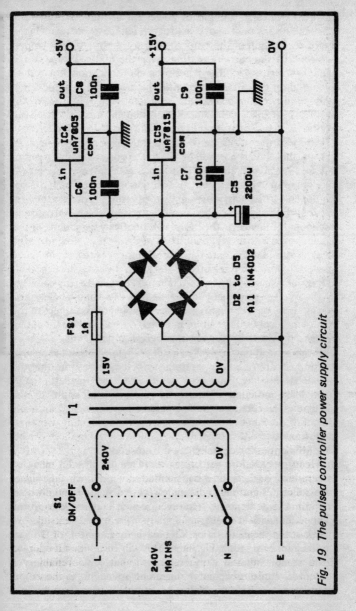

Fig. 19 The pulsed controller power supply circuit

dissipating a large amount of power for a while. Without any heatsinking any fault or overload of this nature would result in the rapid destruction of the output transistor despite the protection afforded by the current limiting (even the foldback type of the circuit of Figure 19). The heatsink and output transistor can be mounted on the circuit board with the other small components, and it will not then be essential to insulate the output transistor from its heatsink, as the latter will presumably not be in electrical contact with any other part of the circuit.

Although the output transistor does not have to dissipate much power, the same is not true of IC5 in the power supply circuit of Figure 19. This will dissipate a few watts with the train running (at or close to) maximum speed, and will soon be destroyed if it is not equipped with at least a medium size heatsink. Probably the best way of providing it with good heatsinking is to use a metal case and to mount the device on the case, or alternatively to mount it on the circuit board with an aluminium bracket being used to conduct the heat away and pass it into the case. In either case there should be no need to insulate IC5 from the bracket or the case, since its heattab connects internally to its "common" terminal. This connects to the 0 volt supply rail of course, and the case should be earthed to this anyway. The mains earth lead should also connect to the case, and a solder tag can be mounted on one of T1's mounting bolts to provide a convenient chassis connection point.

If the +5 volt output of the circuit of Figure 19 is not required, C6 and C8 are of course omitted, as well as IC4. Note that the 100nF decoupling capacitors for the voltage regulator chips should be mounted as close as reasonably possible to the regulators in order to make them fully effective.

Adjustment
With the pulsed controller there is a preset potentiometer (VR1) to be adjusted before the unit is ready for use. If a DC coupled oscilloscope is available, it is just a matter of monitoring the signal at pin 1 of IC2 and then adjusting VR1 to bring the signal within the 0 to 2.5 volt range, making sure that it does not become clipped on negative peaks.

It is still possible to set up VR1 correctly without the aid of an oscilloscope, and probably the easiest way of achieving this is to first output a value of 31 to the digital to analogue converter, or whatever value corresponds to maximum speed for the number of bits you are using (15 for 4 bits, 63 for 6 bits, 127 for 7 bits, and 255 for 8 bits). Then adjust the wiper of VR1 just far enough down towards the R3 end of its track to give full speed from the train. Sending lower values to the train should give a decrease in speed, with power being totally cut off with a value of zero sent to the port.

Unfortunately, the type of electric motor used in model trains often requires a substantial drive voltage before it will start to operate, and although with (say) 5 bit operation there is theoretically 31 speeds plus "off", in practice it is almost certain that some of the lower speed values will not actually cause the train to move. This obviously gives a lower number of speeds that are genuinely available, but there should still be a wide enough range to give good results with 5 bit operation, and with 6 bit operation there will be little or no noticeable change in speed from one speed value to the next.

In Use

The most interesting way of using the unit is as part of an automatic or semiautomatic system, but this really needs sensors to provide feedback in order to give good results. It would obviously be quite possible to program the train to do something like steadily accelerate away, go at full speed for a minute or two, decelerate and stop, wait a minute, and then accelerate away in the opposite direction, or something of this type. The problem with a simple set up of this type is that there is no way of controlling exactly where the train stops, and if it should happen to actually stop at a station it would be by sheer luck. Sensors and feedback are subjects which will be covered in some detail in the next chapter, and they will not be discussed further here.

These controllers can be used as manual types with the aid of appropriate software, and things like simulated breaking and inertia are easily programmed into the system. It would be quite easy to achieve control via the keyboard or using a joystick if preferred (provided your computer supports this feature of course). It is not possible to give software here for a range of computers, since there are so many different computers in common use, and even something as fundamental as reading the keyboard varies somewhat from one computer to another, and one version of BASIC to another.

Software to control model railways does not need to be particularly complex though, and it is well within the scope of a beginner at programming. Acceleration can be achieved by monitoring a particular key and using a simple loop to repeatedly increment the speed variable and output it to the computer. Deceleration can be achieved in much the same way, but with the variable being decremented by one on each loop when a different key is operated. Computers operate quite rapidly even when running a relatively slow language such as BASIC, and delay loops will certainly be needed to slow things down so that the train accelerates and decelerates reasonably realistically. Otherwise the "accelerate" and "decelerate" keys will operate more like "start" and "stop" switches. A point you have to watch is that the value written to the output port does not exceed the maximum speed value, or become negative. This merely requires catch lines, something along the lines of "IF SPEED is less than 0 THEN SPEED = 0: IF SPEED is greater than 31 THEN SPEED = 31.

If you are using the output port for something other than speed control, such as for controlling the direction of the train, the variable containing the speed value must be processed to take this into account before it is sent to the port. This again just needs a simple program line of this general type; "IF DIRECTION=0 THEN SPEED = SPEED + 0: IF DIRECTION = 1 THEN SPEED=SPEED+128". Here we are assuming that the direction of the train is held by the computer in the form of variable "DIRECTION", which is 0 for one direction and 128 for the other. We are also assuming that the direction control relay is controlled by bit 7 of the output port, and the value written to the port therefore has to be boosted by 128 in order to switch on the relay.

Train control software does not need to be complex in order to achieve good results, but it is necessary to take a reasonably well structured approach to things, and to experiment a little in order to fine tune things for optimum results. Of course, if you have the necessary programming experience, then things such as an on-screen representation of the layout with the positions of the trains displayed are perfectly possible.

Manual Control

As an alternative to having a program to give manual control of the unit, you may prefer to have additional hardware to give switched manual/computer operation, and this has the advantage of giving manual control at the flick of a switch without any need to load new software. The circuit diagram of Figure 20 shows how manual control can be added to either the constant voltage or pulsed controllers. Of course, this option is not available if you

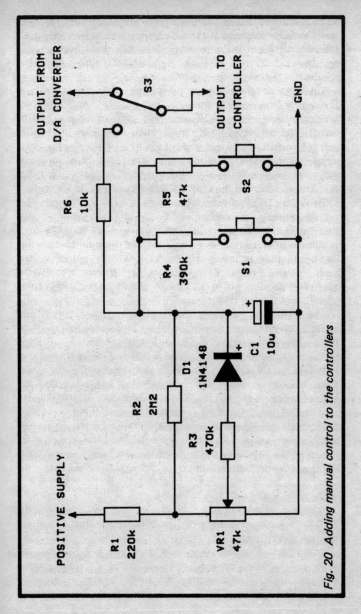

Fig. 20 Adding manual control to the controllers

opt for the software driven pulsed controller. It works best with the hardware implemented pulsed controller which has good enough starting and slow speed performance to do full justice to this method of cortrol. With the constant voltage controller results will be less convincing.

VR1 provides the basic control voltage for the controller, and R1 merely limits the maximum output voltage from VR1 which would otherwise be excessive. For straightforward manual control the output of VR1 can be used directly as the control voltage, but more sophisticated control is possible using the C – R delaying components included in this circuit. One effect of these is to give simulated inertia to the controller. This is provided by R2, R3, D1, and C1, and the effect of these when VR1 is advanced is to provide a delay of a few seconds between VR1 being set for certain voltage and the voltage fed to the controller actually building up to this potential. Thus, setting VR1 instantly from minimum to maximum speed will result in the train accelerating away and only reaching full speed over a period of several seconds. This is reasonably true to life in that it limits the maximum acceleration of the train to something more in keeping with that of the real thing.

The circuit also provides simulated inertia, as backing off VR1 again results in the output voltage taking several seconds to adjust to the new level. In fact the delay is longer than when VR1 is advanced, since D1 cuts R3 out of circuit and the only discharge path for C1 is via R2 and VR1. This is again reasonably true to life, since reducing the power fed to the motor of a real train does not result in it instantly stopping, and it could in fact coast for miles.

Breaking is provided by operating S1, and this gives C1 an additional discharge path through R4 so that the charge voltage decays more rapidly. S2 acts as the emergency break, and when operated this discharges C1 through the relatively low resistance of R5 so that the train is very rapidly brought to a halt. In fact the emergency break will almost certainly bring the train to a standstill even if VR1 is left at maximum speed.

R6 is a protection resistor and S3 is used to switch between the digital to analogue converter (and computer control) and the manual control circuit.

The values shown in Figure 20 should give good results, but they can be changed if you would prefer different control characteristics. The maximum acceleration rate is controlled mainly by the value of R3, and it is roughly proportional to the value of this component. Similarly, R2 controls the time taken for the train to coast to a halt, and the breaking rates are determined by the values of R4 (normal) and R5 (emergency).

If manual control of the train's direction is required, the easiest way of obtaining this is to use a simple over-ride switch in the relay driver circuit, as shown in Figure 21. Here it is assumed that the computer is either not switched on, or that its outputs have been set low so that the relay is normally in the off state. S4 can then be used to switch the relay on or off, as desired.

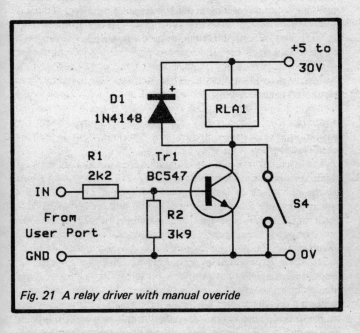

Fig. 21 A relay driver with manual overide

Components for Manual Override Circuit (Fig. 20)
Resistors (all ¼ watt 5%)

R1	220k
R2	2M2
R3	470k
R4	390k
R5	47k
R6	10k

Potentiometer
VR1   47k lin

Capacitor
C1   10µ 25V elect

Semiconductor
D1   1N4148

Miscellaneous
S1   Push to make release to break type
S2   Push to make release to break type
S3   SPDT miniature toggle switch

N.B.
For direction control a SPST miniature toggle switch (S4 of Figure 21) is also required.

Components for Relay Driver with Manual Overide (Fig. 21)
Resistors (all ¼ watt 5% unless noted)
R1   2k2
R2   3k9

Semiconductors
D1   1N4148
Tr1   BC547

Miscellaneous
S4   SPST switch

Boosted Current
In all the controller circuits described in this chapter it has been assumed that a maximum output current of 1 amp is adequate, and with most model trains this should indeed be perfectly adequate. I have not come across any OO gauge or smaller gauge model engines which require greater supply currents than this, even when pulling a large amount of rollingstock. However, if you should happen to have engines that require more current it is possible to modify the circuits to provide it.

In fact the controllers can provide currents of up to at least 2 amps without any modification, apart from the fact that the

increased current means increased dissipa.....
transistor, which accordingly has a greater minimu.
requirement. If you are using a metal case as the heatsi...
almost certainly still prove to be adequate though. If you are ,
to use a ready-made heatsink, then a slightly larger type would b.
preferable, and one with a rating of about 2.6 degrees Centigrade
per watt will ensure that the device keeps well within tolerable
limits. The other point to bear in mind is that the current limit
resistor must be reduced in value in order to permit the higher
output current to flow, and this means reducing it from 0.68 ohms
to 0.33 ohms. The power rating of the resistor should be raised
from 1 watt to 2 watts. With the pulsed controller design the
power supply provides the current limiting, and only permits a
maximum output of 1 amp. Higher current monolithic voltage
regulators are available though, and the most suitable type is the
78S15 which is a 15 volt 2 amp type. Of course, with any of the
designs the mains transformer, rectifiers and fuse must all be types
capable of handling the extra current, and this means using a
mains transformer with a secondary current rating of 3 amps or
more, 1N5402 rectifiers, and a 2 amp fuse.

Chapter 2

POSITION SENSING

Controlling a model train from a computer is half the problem solved, but for sophisticated control it is essential for the computer to keep track of the train's position on the track. It is not really necessary for the computer to be able to follow the progress of the train on an inch by inch basis, and although an arrangement as sophisticated as this could have its advantages, it would make things very complex and difficult as far as the controlling software was concerned. Being realistic about it, basically all that is needed is a system which tells the computer when the train has reached one or two strategic points on the line.

In its most fundamental form the system has a single position sensor fitted (say) some way up the line ahead of a station. By sensing that the train is at that position on the track, the computer can decelerate the train and stop it quite accurately in the station. Of course, in order to get this to work properly it would be necessary to indulge in a little experimentation with the software in order to get the train to slow down and stop in the right place, or alternatively the position sensor would have to be moved around a little until the correct position on the track was located.

Things can be made easier by using two position sensors, with one placed ahead of the station as before, and the other placed in the station nearly at the end of the platform. The idea of this set up is to have the train decelerate down to a slow speed after it passes the first sensor, and then to cruise along very slowly until it reaches the second sensor, whereupon it is brought to a halt. This does not only reduce the amount of experimentation needed in order to get things just right, but also gives much better accuracy with excellent repeatability.

Optical Sensors

There are almost endless ways of sensing the train as it passes, ranging from simple electro-mechanical devices to quite exotic semiconductor sensors. Which type represents the best one to choose is debatable, and depends on what criteria you consider to be most important. There are very inexpensive ways of tackling the problem, but these are often difficult to implement properly in practice, have poor reliability, and may be difficult to conceal

even moderately well. On the other hand, some of the ▨▨▨▨
alternatives are too expensive for most people to co▨▨▨
seriously, and do not necessarily have a level of performan▨▨
which is commensurate with their cost.

Here we will consider a few alternatives, all of which are
reasonably simple to implement in a practical layout, are reliable
in operation, and will not cost more than the train they are
sensing. We will start with simple optical sensors.

Perhaps the obvious type of sensor to use is the broken beam
type, where a beam of light is shone across the track to a light
sensor on the other side. When the train passes between the light
emitter and the sensor it cuts off the light from the sensor, and a
circuit detects the removal of the light and sends a signal to the
computer. In a practical set up of this type the beam is usually an
infra-red one so that it is invisible, and this also renders it a little
less vulnerable to spurious triggering by the ambient light. Better
results and a longer range can be obtained by using a modulated
beam system where the light source provides a series of pulses,
since it is easy to design a circuit which can reliably discriminate
between a strong background light level and a weak pulse signal.

An advantage of this system is that it can be used to span a
double track, or any number of tracks in fact, although in a
practical set up this could be more of a disadvantage than an
advantage since it leaves the system open to misleading results. It
will detect a train on any of the lines that are spanned by the
system, but it will not indicate which line the train is on. It can
consequently only be used in this way provided things are
arranged in such a way that two trains never cross at that
particular point on the track, or even come close at that point. A
disadvantage of this system is that it is double ended, making it
relatively difficult to install and to disguise the two units.

For this application I prefer the slightly different approach of
using the transmitter and receiver sensors side-by-side and aimed
in the same direction. With this system it is not a lack of signal that
the receiver must detect, but the reflected light from a passing
train. This system does not provide very good range, but in this
application this is not really an important consideration as the unit
can be mounted quite close to the track if necessary, and a range
of as little as ten millimetres would probably be perfectly usable.

We will start with a system that operates on the reflected light
principle, but as we shall see later, it can easily be modified to act
as a broken beam type detector. The block diagram of Figure 22

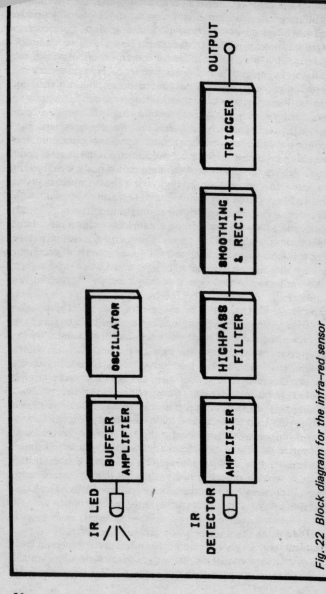

Fig. 22 Block diagram for the infra-red sensor

osc... general arrangement used in the unit.
obtain... ...tter section is very simple, and is basically jus...
driven at a ... an infra-red light emitting diode. In order...
oscillator by w...utput from the light emitting diode it must be
frequency of the osc...rrent, and it is therefore driven from the
be more than a few tens o...fer amplifier. The exact operating
diode, and possibly other pa...tz or the infra-red light emitting
operate at top efficiency. A ve...he circuit as well, will not
problems at the receiver where larg... frequency would give
smoothing capacitors would be needed ...pling capacitors and
results. Also, a low operating frequency would ...der to give good
filter out 100Hz mains hum from electric lighting, whic... ...bout ... it difficult to
the only likely source of interference with a pulsed beam system.
A frequency of around 10kHz offers optimum results.

Note that although the infra-red signal is produced by a light emitting diode, it is perhaps not very aptly named as it does not produce any noticeable output in the visible part of the light spectrum. If you can not see any light output from the finished unit do not worry about it as it does not indicate a fault in the transmitter.

The detector at the receiver is a photo-transistor. There is the possible alternative of a large area photodiode with a built-in infra-red filter but no lens, but in this application the photo-transistor is probably the more suitable, and the directivity provided by the lens largely compensates for the lack of a filter to eliminate visible light. The output signal from the detector device is unlikely to be anything other than quite weak, and a fairly high gain amplifier is used to boost the signal to a usable level. A highpass filter attenuates any mains hum on the signal and prevents the unit from being held in the "on" state when the train is not within its field of view. The amplified signal is rectified and smoothed to give a strong positive output, but only if a significant amount of signal is reflected back to the receiver. A trigger circuit at the output of the unit converts this relatively small voltage swing into a signal that is compatible with logic inputs.

Pulse Detection

A problem that has to be borne in mind when dealing with sensors is that of making sure that the output signal is present long enough for it to be reliably detected by the software. The input line into

For th~~is~~ type of application edge sensitive inputs are extremely
good. With these it is not the static state of the input line that is
monitored, but a transition from one logic level to another. The
way in which this generally works is that the interface device has a
register which contains a number of status flags, and when an
active transition occurs on an edge sensitive input line one of these
flags is set. It then remains in this state until it is reset by the
program, and this avoids any risk of the input signal being missed,
even if it lasts a mere microsecond or two.

As a simple example of how an edge triggered input is used in
practice we will consider line CB1 of the BBC computer's user
port. This handshake line is an uncomplicated type which has only
two operating modes, and in both of these it functions as an edge
sensitive input. The operating mode is set using the Peripheral
Control Register at address &FE6C, and in the case of CB1 it is
only bit 4 of this register that is of interest. Setting this bit low
(?&FE6C=0) places CB1 in the high to low handshake mode,
whereas setting it to 1 (?&FE6C=16) places CB1 in the high to
low handshake mode. In other words, with the control bit set low
it is a transition from the high state to the low one which sets the
flag, while it is a transition from the low state to the high one which
sets the flag if the control bit is set high.

The flag is bit 4 of the Interrupt Flag Register at address
&FE6D, and this bit can be read with the aid of the bitwise AND
function (i.e. PRINT ?&FE6D AND 16 will return a value of 16 if
this flag is set, or 0 if it is not). The flag can be reset by a read or
write operation to the user port, or by writing 1 to the flag itself
(i.e. ?&FE6D=16). This is fairly typical of the way handshake
lines operate, but obviously technical details of the parallel port of

your particular computer will be needed in order to make use of any handshake inputs that are available. A data sheet for the interface device concerned would also be more than a little useful.

Another important factor to keep in mind when dealing with sensors is that they may not be activated only when the train first approaches, and may be activated for the whole time that the train passes. In fact most types of sensor probably fall into this catagory. This could be useful, but it has the potential to crash the system if the software is fooled into thinking that these extra operations of the sensor are totally new ones, rather than just continuations of the previous one. This problem is easily overcome by using a delay to hold off further reading of the sensor until the train has had time to pass by, or perhaps by monitoring the output from the sensor and just looping the program until no triggering has occured for a certain period of time, and then taking the program back into its normal mode of operation.

Transmitter

Returning to the infra-red sensor, the circuit diagram of the transmitter section appears in Figure 23. This is based on a 555 astable (oscillator) circuit and timing components R1, R2, and C2 give a roughly squarewave output at a frequency of a few kilohertz. Tr1 is the buffer amplifier, and this operates as a common emitter switch. IC1 could in theory provide sufficient output current to directly drive the light emitting diode (D1), but in reality this could prove to be difficult, particularly with the low supply voltage of 5 volts, as the LED current could not be set with even moderately good accuracy. In this circuit R4 sets the LED current at something approaching 100 milliamps, but as the LED is switched off for almost 50% of the time the average LED current is approximately 50 milliamps.

Components for Infra-red Transmitter (Fig. 23)
Resistors (all ¼ watt 5% unless noted)

R1	1k
R2	47k
R3	1k
R4	33R (½ watt)

Capacitors

C1	470µ 10V elect
C2	4n7 polyester

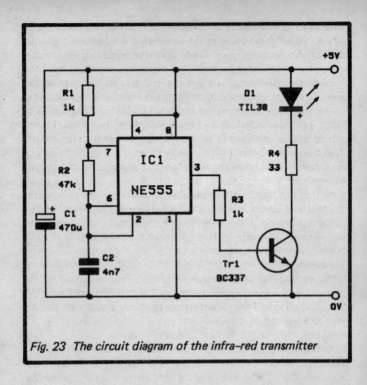

Fig. 23 The circuit diagram of the infra-red transmitter

Semiconductors

IC1	NE555
Tr1	BC337
D1	TIL38

Miscellaneous
Case
Circuit board
Holder for D1
8 pin DIL IC holder
Wire, solder, etc.

Receiver

Figure 24 shows the receiver circuit, and here Tr1 is the photo-transistor. The base terminal is left unconnected, and the collector – emitter leakage provides a sort of simple photoresistor action. In conjunction with R1 this resistance forms a potential divider across the supply lines, and the variations in leakage current produced by the pulses of infra-red radiation from the transmitter produce small voltage pulses that are fed to the amplifier stage. This is a single high gain common emitter stage based on Tr2 and driving an emitter follower buffer stage. The latter gives the amplifier a low output impedance so that a fast attack time is obtained from the rectifier and smoothing circuit. This is a conventional twin diode type based on D1 and D2. The high value of R6 gives the required long decay time of a second or two.

IC1 is the trigger circuit which provides a logic compatible output, and this is just an operational amplifier connected as a voltage comparator. Note though, that few operational amplifiers will operate properly with a 5 volt supply, and that fewer still would provide adequate output current and voltage levels to drive logic devices properly. You should not therefore, try to substitute other operational amplifiers for the CA3130E specified for the IC1 position. Even this device may not drive standard TTL devices properly, but it seems to work well with CMOS, PMOS, and low power TTL devices.

Components for Infra-red Receiver (Fig. 24)
Resistors (all ¼ watt 5%)

R1	15k
R2	1M
R3	4k7
R4	1k
R5	1k
R6	1M

Potentiometer

VR1	10k sub-min hor preset

Capacitors

C1	100μ 10V elect
C2	10n polyester
C3	1μ 63V elect
C4	2μ2 63V elect
C5	100μ 10V elect

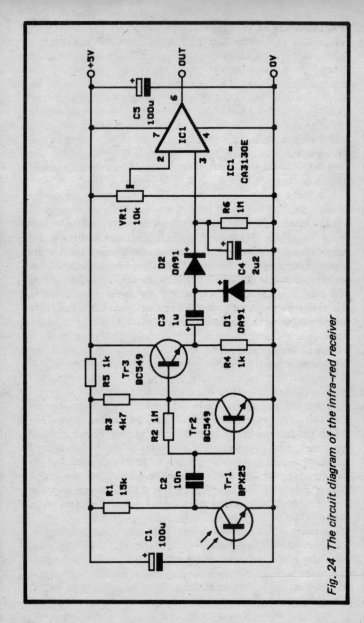

Fig. 24 The circuit diagram of the infra-red receiver

62

Semiconductors

Tr1	BPX25
Tr2	BC549
Tr3	BC549
IC1	CA313OE
D1	OA91
D2	OA91

Miscellaneous
Circuit board
8 pin DIL IC holder
Wire, solder, etc.

Construction

There is nothing particularly difficult from the constructional
point of view, but obviously the unit must be arranged so that D1
in the transmitter and Tr1 in the receiver are mounted side-by-
side with their lenses "looking" out through holes in the case of
the unit. These two components do not need to be mounted
practically in contact with one another, but on the other hand they
should not be much more than about 20 millimetres or so apart.
They need to be partitioned off from one another to prevent direct
pick-up of the output from the LED by the phototransistor. Long
unscreened leads at the input of the amplifier should be avoided,
but the gain of the amplifier is not high enough to make stray pick-
up or instability due to stray feedback major problems.

D1 and D2 are germanium diodes, and these are far less hardy
than the more common silicon diodes. In particular they are
vulnerable to damage by heat and care should be taken when
soldering them into circuit. It is probably not worthwhile using a
heatshunt on each leadout wire as it is soldered into place, but the
soldering iron should not be applied to each joint for any longer
than is absolutely necessary. IC1 is a CMOS device and the
standard antistatic handling precautions should be taken when
dealing with this component.

The range of the system is largely dependent on just how well
(or otherwise) the target object reflects infra-red radiation. With
something like a good mirror set to accurately reflect the signal
back to the receiving sensor a range of half a metre or more might
be achieved, but with most objects the range is likely to be 150
millimetres or less. High sensitivity is not really a great advantage

63

in this application, and a range of 150 millimetres should be more than adequate. If the train proves to be a poor reflector of infra-red the unit should still provide an adequate range, since as little as 25 to 50 millimetres should be quite usable, and this is about the minimum you are likely to obtain. Obviously the unit needs to be positioned at a suitable height so that it is reflecting the beam off the flat side of the engine and rolling stock, rather than trying to reflect the beam off the wheels (which would almost certainly give insufficient returned signal to activate the unit). For optimum sensitivity the unit should be at right angles to the train. Neither the transmitting or receiving photocells are highly directional, and the aim should not need to be highly accurate in order to get good results.

It is quite possible that the range will be adequate to encompass both tracks of a twin track layout, which might be something you wish to exploit, or it might prove to be something of a problem. If necessary the range can be reduced somewhat by raising the value of R4 in the transmitter. In theory at any rate, raising the value of this component by a factor of four, halves the maximum range of the unit.

Reading the Sensor
The use of edge triggered handshake inputs was covered earlier, but this unit will operate well with an ordinary input. Using an 8 bit input/output port of the type fitted on the BBC machine it is perfectly feasable to have an arrangement along the lines of the least significant six bits used for speed and direction control, with the two most significant bits set as inputs to monitor a couple of sensors. The bitwise AND function can be used to monitor just one input while ignoring the others, and to monitor (say) bit 7, the number with which the value returned from the port would be ANDed is 128. In other words, the value used is equal to the value contributed by the input line concerned when it is set to the high state. It is possible to monitor two or more inputs, and the value used to do this is then simply equal to the sum of the numbers that would be used to monitor each of the lines individually. For example, a value of 192 (64 plus 128) would be used to monitor bits 6 and 7. The returned values would then be 0 if no lines are high, 64 if line 6 is high, 128 if line 7 is high, or 192 if both lines are high.

Although most (probably all) BASICs have an AND function, they do not all support a bitwise AND version of it, or have the same function by some other name (BAND in the case of Enterprise computers for example). All the popular microprocessors such as the 6502 and Z80 have bitwise AND instructions, and so this function is available at machine code level. Another way of reading an input is to feed it into the most significant line. The value read from the input port will then be 128 or more if the line is high, or less than 128 if it is not, and any version of BASIC should permit this simple test to determine the state of the line.

Broken Beam

The circuit will work perfectly well as a broken beam detector, but when used in this way it is advisable to make a few changes in some component values in order to optimise results. The system will almost certainly provide an adequate range with the transmitter's output power greatly reduced, and R4 in the transmitter can be made much higher in value (about 330 ohms should suffice). At the receiver the long decay time of the smoothing circuit is undesirable, and could result in the train passing undetected under certain conditions. This can be corrected by reducing C4 from $2\mu2$ to 470n, and reducing R6 from 1M to 100k.

The circuit will have an output that is normally high, and which goes low when the beam is broken. This should be perfectly satisfactory in use provided the software is designed to suit this scheme of things. However, by simply swopping the connections to IC1's inputs (pins 2 and 3) the circuit will provide a normally low output level which goes high when the beam is broken.

Shadow Detector

The infra-red detector represents a reasonably simple form of sensor that is very reliable and convenient in use, but there are even more simple alternatives which are adequate for most purposes. My preferred type of sensor is the shadow detector type, which is based on a photocell mounted in the middle of the track facing upwards. As the train passes over it the light level received by the sensor is reduced, and it is this that the circuit must detect.

An arrangement of this type is not totally reliable in that it must be to some extent dependent on the ambient light level being suitable, and in very low or high light levels the unit could fail to work. It is also open to spurious triggering if someone, or something other than the model train should happen to cast a shadow over the photocell.

In a practical situation a unit of this type can be made to operate with perfectly adequate reliability, with correct operation being provided over the range of light levels likely to be encountered in a domestic environment, and only quite strong shadows being adequate to trigger the unit. Figure 25 shows the circuit diagram of a simple shadow detector.

Tr1 is the light detector, and this offers good sensitivity combined with reasonably small size and fast switching speed. Although a BPX25 is specified for the Tr1 position, any similar device such as the TIL81 or BPY62 is equally suitable (the same is also true of Tr1 in the infra-red receiver incidentally). No connection is made to the base terminal of Tr1. Under quiescent conditions Tr1 will pass a substantial leakage current, giving a fairly low potential at its collector terminal. When the train passes over Tr1 it is placed under darker conditions and a lower leakage current flows. This causes a sudden increase in its collector voltage, and this is coupled to the input of a high gain common emitter amplifier by C2. There is an inversion through Tr2, so that a strong negative going signal is generated at its collector terminal.

IC1 is a low power CMOS version of the popular 555 timer integrated circuit, and here it is used in the monostable mode. Its purpose is to convert the signal at the collector of Tr2 into a logic compatible (positive) output pulse of a second or so in duration. R6 and C4 are the timing components, and with the specified values the nominal output pulse duration is 1.1 seconds. R4 and R5 bias the trigger input to about half the supply voltage under quiescent conditions, and this holds IC1 in the untriggered state since this input must be taken below one third of the supply voltage in order to activate the circuit. When the train passes over Tr1 and the negative output signal is produced by Tr2, C3 couples this signal to the trigger input of IC1 so that the monostable is activated.

Components for Shadow Detector (Fig. 25)
Resistors (all ¼ watt 5%)

R1	10k
R2	1M
R3	4k7

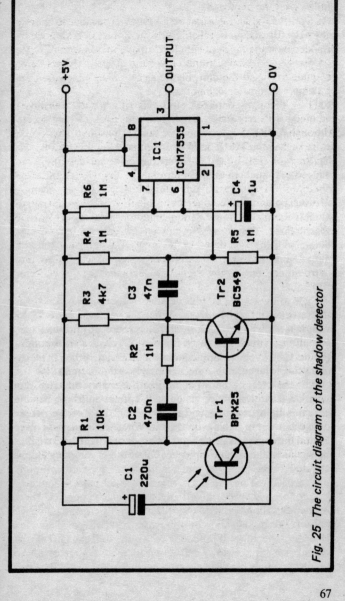

Fig. 25 The circuit diagram of the shadow detector

67

R4	1M
R5	1M
R6	1M

Capacitors

C1	220μ 10V elect
C2	470n polyester
C3	47n polyester
C4	1μ 63V elect

Semiconductors

IC1	ICM7555
Tr1	BPX25 or similar
Tr2	BC549

Miscellaneous
Circuit board
Plastic case
Screened lead
8 pin DIL IC holder
Wire, solder, etc.

Construction

Construction of this circuit should not present any problems, and the printed circuit design of Figures 26 (copper track) and 27 (component overlay) should make things easier, although the unit could easily be built on a piece of stripboard if preferred.

Although IC1 is a CMOS device, it has very effective static protection circuits which render the normal antistatic handling precautions totally unnecessary. It would be difficult or even impossible to build this project in the form of a single unit placed between the rails of a track, and a more practical approach is to build the unit as a normal project but with Tr1 remotely located. Construction is then very much more straightforward as only Tr1 has to be fitted on the track, and it is small enough for this to present no great problems. It might not even be necessary to cut or modify the piece of track to which Tr1 is fitted, and it might be possible to simply glue it or otherwise fix it between a couple of sleepers. The unit will probably work quite well even if Tr1 is not aimed straight upwards, and a considerable degree of tilt will almost certainly be perfectly acceptable. From the physical point

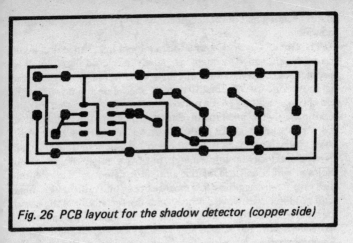

Fig. 26 PCB layout for the shadow detector (copper side)

of view the main points to watch are that the device is firmly fixed in place so that vibration does not cause spurious operation of the unit, and that it does not protrude too far above the sleepers (which at best will derail the occasional passing train).

Tr1 should be connected to the main unit via a piece of screened cable, as stray pick up of the large amount of electrical noise surrounding the average model railway layout will otherwise cause spurious triggering of the unit. The emitter connects to the

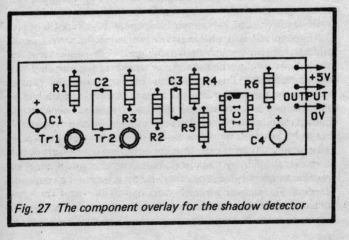

Fig. 27 The component overlay for the shadow detector

outer braiding and the collector connection is carried by the inner conductor.

The circuit will work over a wide ambient light range, but avoid having Tr1 aimed straight at mains powered lighting. The problem here is not so much the high light level saturating Tr1, but is more one of the mains "hum" modulated onto the light producing a 100Hz output signal from Tr2 that would continuously trigger the unit. Saturation of the unit is unlikely to be a problem at all, as with Tr1 under very bright light under stand-by conditions, it is still likely that the light level as the train passes over will be low enough to give a small rise in output voltage which will trigger the unit. Insufficient light preventing the unit from triggering is a stronger possibility, although this is still not likely. However, if necessary the sensitivity of the circuit can be boosted by making R1 higher in value. The circuit is a passive sensor, and as such it will always need some ambient light in order to work properly.

Magnetic Sensor
Magnetic sensors have been popular in the past, but have to some extent been replaced by opto-sensors in recent years. However, magnetic sensors are still a useful and workable solution to the problem, and are certainly worthy of consideration. There are two basic types of magnetic sensor; reed switches and Hall Effect switches. The latter are semiconductor devices, and although they can work well in this application they are generally more expensive and difficult to obtain than reed switches.

Reed switches are very simple components which consist of two pieces of springy wire placed end to end, but slightly overlapping and not quite in contact with one another. These pieces of wire, or "reeds" as they are called, are made from a magnetic material, but are not normally magnetised. However, if a magnet is brought close to the reeds, they become temporarily magnetised, and as the two ends that are close together are opposite magnetic poles, mutual attraction causes them to touch together. When the magnet is removed they become demagnetised and spring apart. The two reeds can therefore be brought into electrical contact with one another by a magnetic field, and contact can then be broken again by removing the field, giving a magnetically controlled mechanical switching action.

The usual arrangement is for the reeds to be contained in a glass envelope with the reeds extended to form leadout wires, or attached to separate leadout wires, as shown in Figure 28. The voltage and current ratings of reed switches are generally quite low, but are nevertheless considerably more than adequate for the present application.

In order to operate as a position sensor on a model railway layout it is no use simply having the reed switch mounted on or in the track. There is an outside chance that this would work since the electric motors used in model trains are of a type which utilizes permanent magnets as well as having electro-magnets. In practice though, it is unlikely that these fields would prove to be adequate to operate a reed switch. The switch or switches must therefore be complemented by a bar magnet on each train (they do not work well with other types of magnet).

Suppliers of reed switches can often supply matching bar magnets to operate them. In general it is probably best to opt for the smallest reed switches and magnets that you can obtain, as apart from being the easiest as far as installation is concerned, they generally give the best range. In fact it is the small reed switches that generally offer the best sensitivity, and a large magnet will often give better results than a smaller and (probably) less powerful type. It might therefore be better to use a small reed switch and a large magnet, provided of course, that the train can accommodate the larger magnet. With any combination the range is not likely to be very great, and something in the region of 5 to 25 millimetres is quite typical.

In order to obtain sufficient operating distance it is essential to have the reed switch and magnet correctly orientated in relation to one another, and considerable thought needs to be exercised before trying to install either of them. The main point to bear in mind is that it is not one pole of the magnet that should be applied to the reed in order to operate it. The reed switch and the magnet must be parallel to one another, and in the current application this gives only two basic methods of installation. Either the reed switch can be mounted across the track between two sleepers with the magnet mounted across the floor of a truck or other piece of rollingstock, or the reed switch must be mounted down the middle of the track with the magnet similarly mounted on the floor and down the centre of a piece of rollingstock. Ideally the reed switch would be mounted across the track and out of sight beneath it, with the magnet fitted inside a piece of rollingstock, and again out of sight. This is perfectly feasible provided the combination of reed switch and magnet that you use provides an operating range

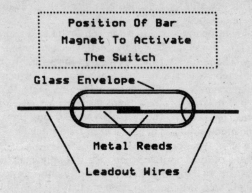

Fig. 28 A reed switch is a very simple type of switch
which takes the form depicted here

of around 20 millimetres or more. Otherwise the distance
between the two is likely to be too large and the switch will not be
activated, but the minimum range for this system obviously
depends on the particular pieces of rollingstock in use, the type of
track, and the gauge of the layout. If a compromise has to be
made, it is probably best to move the magnet to the underside of
the truck (or whatever) rather than to move the reed switch up
above the level of the sleepers where it could tend to derail passing
trains unless you were very careful about its exact positioning.

Unlike the methods of sensing described previously, the
magnet and reed switch combination provides only a momentary
switching action as the train passes. This can be used with edge
triggered inputs without any difficulty, and all that is needed is a
simple circuit of the type shown in Figure 29. In (a) the circuit
produces a negative edge as the switch is activated, whereas in (b)
a positive edge is generated as the switch closes. In practice it will
probably not matter which of these circuits is used, or whether the
input line is set to the positive or negative edge triggered mode,

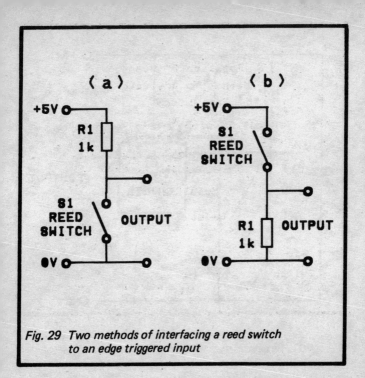

Fig. 29 *Two methods of interfacing a reed switch to an edge triggered input*

since the action of the circuits is to produce a transition of one type as the switch closes, and then a transition of the opposite type when it opens again a fraction of a second later. It is really just a matter of using whichever of the circuits and whichever input mode happens to be the most convenient.

The circuits of Figure 29 are practically useless with an ordinary input line, since there is a very real risk of the brief switching action being missed by a software routine which periodically tests the state of the line. Greater reliability can be obtained by using a monostable multivibrator as a pulse stretcher, as in the circuit diagram of Figure 30.

This is just a 555 monostable circuit triggered by the reed switch. It is really just the same as shadow detector circuit, but with the opto part of the unit replaced by the reed switch.

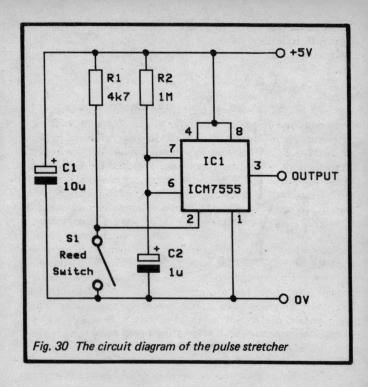

Fig. 30 The circuit diagram of the pulse stretcher

Components for Pulse Stretcher (Fig. 30)
Resistors (all ¼ watt 5%)
R1   4k7
R2   1M

Capacitors
C1   10µ 25V elect
C2   1µ 63V elect

Semiconductor
IC1   ICM7555

Miscellaneous
S1   Miniature reed switch
Circuit board

74

Small plastic case
8 pin DIL IC holder
Wire, solder, etc.

Signals

It is easy to control coloured light type signals from a computer, and a relay and driver represents one way of doing this. In fact it represents quite a good way of tackling the problem as the electrical isolation between the computer and the controlled circuits avoids any earthing problems. Provided the signals are driven from a DC supply with one supply rail properly earthed, the relays will not be necessary and there should be no difficulty in driving the signal lights direct from a common emitter switch. Incidentally, when connecting any mains powered add-on to a computer it is advisable only to do so if either the computer or the add-on (or both) have their earth rail earthed to the mains supply. If neither of the earth rails are properly earthed there is a danger of a fairly high voltage (possibly more than 100 volts) being present between the two earth rails. Although this signal should be at a very high impedance, it is still capable of causing damage to the interface devices in the units if they are directly wired together. Opto-isolators can be used to avoid any problems, but in general it is easier just to earth the negative supply rail (assuming it is negative earth equipment) of the add-on.

If a suitably earthed supply is available, miniature filament bulbs and light emitting diode signals can be driven using the circuits of Figure 31(a) and Figure 31(b) respectively. Anyone with a reasonable amount of model making skill could probably build their own signals using miniature light emitting diodes without too much difficulty, and I have often done so. You can then opt for simple red/green signals, red/green/amber types, or even red/green/amber/double amber signals if preferred. Controlling three or four state signals can be a bit awkward when using ordinary logic circuits for control purposes, but with a computer controlled system there is no real difficulty as it is just a matter of sending the appropriate values to the output port in order to switch on the required signal lights.

It is often possible to rationalise things in order to make more economic use of the available output lines by driving two lights from a single output. This can be achieved using the set up shown in the circuit diagram of Figure 32. This circuit is a common

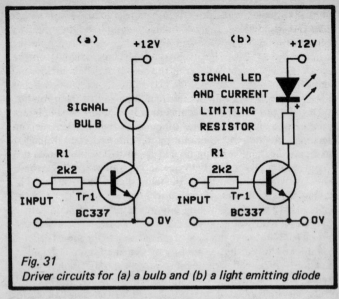

Fig. 31
Driver circuits for (a) a bulb and (b) a light emitting diode

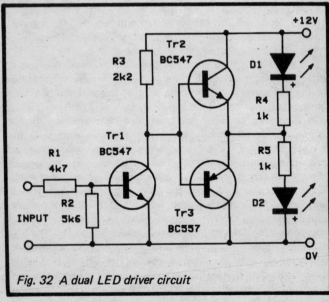

Fig. 32 A dual LED driver circuit

76

emitter switching transistor (Tr1) having a load resistor rather than directly driving a signal light. A complementary emitter follower output stage (Tr2 and Tr3) is then used to enable the switch to drive the two signal lights. A high control signal from the computer switches on Tr1, taking the output of the circuit low and switching on light emitting diode D1. A low input signal switches off Tr1, taking the output of the circuit high and switching on D2.

The obvious limitation of this arrangement is that it is not possible to have both light emitting diodes switched on, or both switched off. This will often not matter though, and D1 and D2 could, for example, be the red and green LEDs of a simple two colour signal.

Components for Dual LED Driver (Fig. 32)
Resistors (all ¼ watt 5% unless noted)

R1	4k7
R2	5k6
R3	2k2
R4	1k
R5	1k

Semiconductors

D1	Suitable Colour LED
D2	Suitable Colour LED
Tr1	BC547
Tr2	BC547
Tr3	BC557

In Use

The signals could be manually controlled with the aid of suitable software, but this would be a rather overcomplicated way of providing simple manual control. It is really automatic operation that makes computer control worthwhile, and there are two standard approaches to this. Both are easily accomplished by a computer controlled system.

The first approach is to have the signal manually controlled, but to have the train automatically respond to the signals. On the face of it this is something that could be handled solely in software, with the train being brought to a halt when the signal is set to "red" via the keyboard, and then started again when it is set to "green". This is not really good enough in practice though, as the train must

77

stop just in front of the signal, and not wherever it happens to be on the track when the signal is set to "red".

In order to work properly this system needs slight refinement with the addition of a sensor to indicate to the computer that the train is approaching the signal, and if the signal is set at "red" the computer can go into a decelerate and stop routine which is designed to bring the train to a halt in the right place. With a three or four state signal the system could be refined still further so that with the signal at amber the train is decelerated down to a slow speed, but is not brought to a standstill. Provided sufficient input and output lines are available, there should be no difficulty in producing a multi-signal set up.

The second method of automatic signalling is one which has definite similarities to the real thing, and it has manual control of the train or trains with the signals being set automatically. This requires a sensor by each signal, and the idea is simply to have each signal set to "red" as the train passes. It is returned to "green" either after a preset period of time has elapsed, or (preferably) after the train has passed a second sensor positioned a suitable distance down the track from the first one. This system can obviously be extended to accommodate three or four state signals, with further preset delays between changes in the signal, or more sensors being used to provide the triggering from one state to another.

This system can operate with manual control of the train via the computer and one of the controllers described in Chapter 1, or the computer can just provide control of the signals with a separate manual controller being used to drive the train or trains.

With a computer based system there is a third alternative, and this is programmed fully automatic operation. With this method the trains and the signals all work to a preprogrammed pattern, with no manual interference with the system at all. Perhaps not a great deal of fun to use, but it is certainly an interesting challenge to get the whole thing running fully automatically with no crashes (in the computer or in the ordinary sense of the word "crash"!).

Points Control

In order to have totally automatic control of anything but the most basic of layouts it is essential to have electric points controlled via a suitable interface. Electric points are really very simple pieces of equipment, and from the electrical point of view thay are just a couple of solenoids. There are usually only three terminals

78

though, as both solenoids connect to a "common" terminal. This is connected to one side of a 12 volt DC supply, and by connecting one or other of the other terminals to the other side of the supply the points can be "set" or "reset".

One way of controlling electric points is to use a couple of relays, with each one providing on/off switching to a solenoid. There are two problems with this arrangement though, and I would strongly advise against its use. One problem is simply that of poor reliability, with the points tending to stick and obviously giving a strong possibility of derailment or one train crashing into another. The other problem is that of the high current that flows when power is applied to a solenoid, and the likelihood of the solenoid burning out unless the time for which power is applied to it is strictly limited.

With a manual controller the standard system is to have a two way switch biased to a central "off" position, so that when the switch is released power is automatically and immediately cut off from both solenoids. With a simple computer controlled system it is up to the programmer to ensure that power is only applied to the solenoids for about one second at a time. While this is not too difficult, there is always a risk of a careless programming error resulting in power being applied for too long, and a solenoid burning out as a result.

By using some simple and inexpensive electronics it is possible to obtain much better reliability, and to virtually eliminate any possibility of a solenoid being burned out. Reliability can be greatly improved by the use of a capacitor discharge system. Really all this means is having a high value capacitor connected across the supply lines so that when the solenoid is activated, this capacitor provides the pulse of high current that is needed to reliably "kick" the points from one setting to the other. The problem of burning out the solenoids can be overcome by feeding the capacitor from the 12 volt supply via a current limiting resistor. This lets only a modest current flow if a solenoid is connected to the power source continuously, but this does not prevent the points from being activated reliably as the charge storage capacitor can still provide the initial large burst of current needed to operate the points. It takes a second or two for the capacitor to recharge via the current limiting resistor, but this should not be noticeable in practice as it would not be necessary to switch the points to one setting and then set them straight back again a couple of seconds later.

In the points interface featured here there is an additional safety measure in the form of a built-in timing circuit which cuts off power to the point after a little under one second regardless of how long the input signal lasts. Also, the unit has been designed to enable single line control of a point where placing the control line high "sets" the point, and placing the line low again "resets" the point. The circuit diagram of the points interface appears in Figures 33 and 34.

Starting with Figure 33, R1 and C1 are respectively the current limiting resistor and charge storage capacitor. Tr1 is the switching device, and this is a power Darlington type. In this application the power it has to dissipate is negligible, but a power Darlington is still a good choice as it provides the very high gain that is essential if the required high output current is to be achieved, and it will not be damaged by the large current pulses. D1 is the usual protection diode to suppress any reverse voltage spike generated across the solenoid as it is switched off.

Tr1 is driven from a monostable multivibrator which is based on two of the CMOS NOR gates of IC1. R3 and C2 are the timing components, and they give an output pulse duration of typically a little under one second. The timing accuracy of a simple monostable of this type is not particularly good, but in the present application quite large timing errors will not adversely affect reliability. The monostable is a positive edge triggered type, and it is non-retriggerable. What this means in practice is that the point is "set" as the input signal goes from a low state to a high one, and that the output pulse duration is independent of the input pulse width.

Turning now to Figure 34, this circuit can be driven from the same output line as the "set" circuit of Figure 33, and it also shares the same current limiting resistor and charge storage capacitor. It is in many ways similar to the "set" circuit, but it is based on a different monostable configuration. This one is negative edge triggered, and is again non-retriggerable. It therefore resets the point as the input signal goes from the high state to the low one.

Construction of the points controller offers nothing out of the ordinary, but remember that both the integated circuits are CMOS types and that they consequently require the usual antistatic handling precautions. Tr1 and Tr2 do not have to dissipate a significant amount of power, and certainly do not require even small heatsinks.

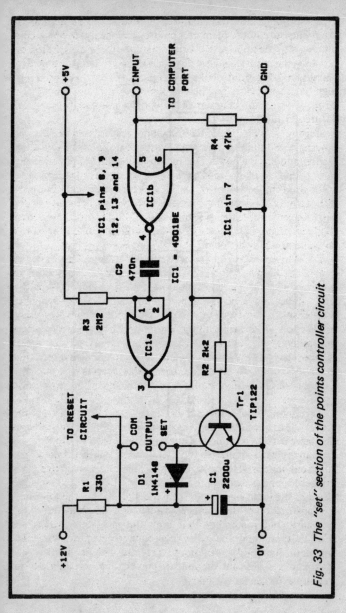

Fig. 33 The "set" section of the points controller circuit

81

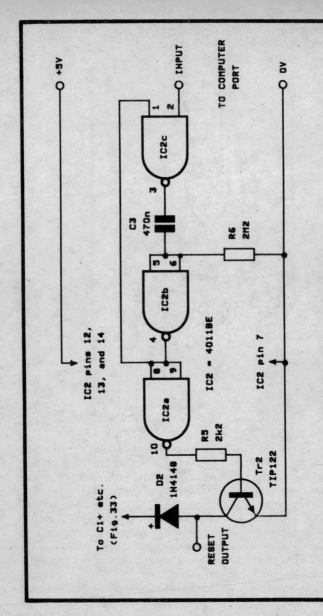

Fig. 34 The circuit diagram of the points controller "reset"

Components for Points Controller (Figs. 33 or 34)
Resistors (all ¼ watt 5% unless noted)

R1	330R (1 watt)
R2	2k2
R3	2M2
R4	47k
R5	2k2
R6	2M2

Capacitors

C1	2200μ 25V elect
C2	470n polyester
C3	470n polyester

Semiconductors

IC1	4001BE
IC2	4011BE
Tr1	TIP122
Tr2	TIP122
D1	1N4148
D2	1N4148

Miscellaneous
Circuit board
Case
Two 14 pin DIL IC holders
Wire, solder, etc.

Sound Effects

Most computers have some form of sound generator, and these can usually give some quite good sound effects. It is not too difficult to add something like a two-tone horn sound effect to a program, with the sound perhaps being triggered by (say) a sensor added just ahead of a level crossing.

If the computer is equipped with a noise channel, as a good many are, then it will be probably be possible to program it to produce the so-called "chuffer" steam train effect. Getting the computer to generate rhythmic bursts of noise to give a "chuffing" sound is unlikely to be very difficult, but this sound effect really needs to be properly synchronised to the speed of the train to be worthwhile. This is less easy since it is only possible if the computer has some way of determining the speed of the train, and this may well produce problems.

If the computer is controlling the speed of the train, then the value that is used to set the speed of the train can also be used in the sound effects part of the program to set the "chuff" rate. This could work quite well, but there is a possible problem in that some computers are not very good at producing sounds while carrying out other tasks. Producing the occasional two-tone horn effect is unlikely to give any serious difficulties, but a continuous "chuffing" sound might take up too much of the computer's time to permit it to do much else.

The alternative way of controlling the "chuff" rate is to take the track voltage and feed it to the input of an analogue to digital converter interface so that the computer can gauge the speed of the train by measuring the track voltage. Unfortunately, few computers are equipped with a built-in analogue to digital converter (the BBC machine being one popular exception), but add-ons of this type are available for some machines. The circuit of Figure 35 can be used to interface the track to the input of a converter having a full scale input voltage of about +5 volts or less. This just consists of a bridge rectifier (D1 to D4) to ensure that the polarity of the signal is correct regardless of the direction in which the train is driven, followed by a smoothing circuit (R1

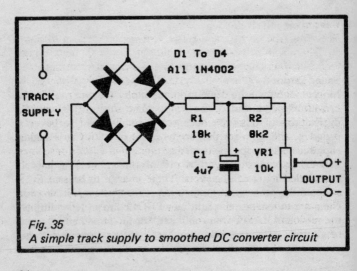

Fig. 35
A simple track supply to smoothed DC converter circuit

and C1). The latter is necessary since many controllers have a pulsed output to which most converters will not respond properly. VR1 is adjusted to give a maximum output voltage that is just within the full scale value of the analogue to digital converter.

You may find it interesting to experiment with computer generated sound effects, but for anything other than a simple two-tone horn effect I would recommend the use of conventional sound effects circuits, leaving the computer free for control purposes.

Components for Smoothed DC Converter (Fig. 35)
Resistors (all ¼ watt 5% unless noted)
R1   18k
R2   8k2

Potentiometer
VR1   10k

Capacitors
C1 $4\mu7$ 25V electrolytic

Semiconductors
D1 – D4   1N4002 (four off)

Conclusion
With this type of system there is a strong temptation to jump straight in with a massive set-up, but unless you are fairly expert with electronics and at programming this is almost certainly the wrong approach. It is probably much better to start with a fairly simple system, and to develop some simple software routines to provide basic control of the layout. The software for control applications of this type does not normally need to be very complex, and a layout that seems to be operating in a highly sophisticated manner might need no more than a dozen or so lines of BASIC to control things. It is certainly the type of thing that can be handled by most beginners. There is a lot to be said for a structured approach to programming in this type of application. If you work out some subroutines or PROCedures (depending on the version of BASIC your computer runs) to provide basic types of control, such as acceleration and deceleration of a train, monitoring of a sensor until a positive result is obtained, and so

on, these can then be used in any control programs that you write for the layout. This makes it relatively easy to start with a simple system and to gradually build it up and extend it. The structured approach tends to be a little slow in operation, but in this application high operating speed is not really needed. You are far more likely to find it necessary to put in delay loops to slow down the program than to find an element of the program responding too slowly. The main thing is to be prepared to experiment a little with the software, and not to expect everything to work perfectly first time. It is easy to write simple routines to accelerate and decelerate a train, but it takes a little more time and care to fine-tune the software to get the acceleration and deceleration characteristics just right. It is well worthwhile putting in the extra effort to get things just right.

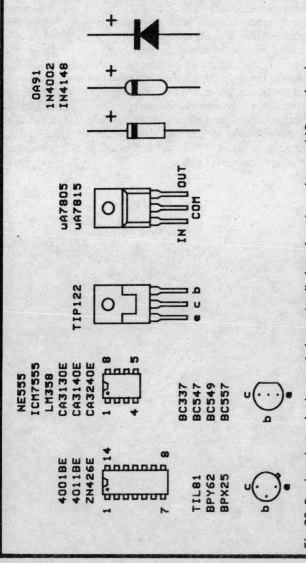

Fig. 36 Semiconductor leadout and pinout details (transistor base views and IC top views)